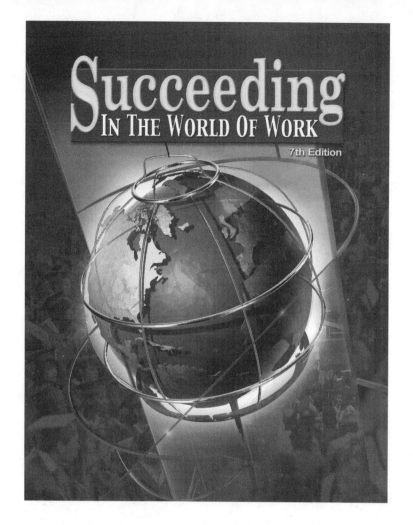

Succeeding IN THE WORLD OF WORK

7th Edition

Student Activity Workbook

Grady Kimbrell
Educational Consultant
Santa Barbara, California
Ben S. Vineyard
Professor and Chairman Emeritus
Vocational and Technical Education
Pittsburg State University
Pittsburg, Kansas

Glencoe McGraw-Hill

New York, New York   Columbus, Ohio   Chicago, Illinois   Peoria, Illinois   Woodland Hills, California

Glencoe/McGraw-Hill

A Division of The McGraw·Hill Companies

Send all inquiries to:
GLENCOE DIVISION
McGraw-Hill
21600 Oxnard Street
Woodland Hills, California 91367

ISBN 0-07-829699-4 (Student Edition)
ISBN 0-07-829700-1 (Teacher Annotated Edition)

Printed in the United States of America.

2 3 4 5 6 7 8 9   009   05 04 03

Table of Contents

Table of Contents

CHAPTER **1** You and the World of Work

ACTIVITY 1-1	**Foundation Skills**
Lifestyle Surveys	*Personal Qualities:* *Self-Management*

Objective: To help you see how working people feel about their lifestyles and careers.

Your choice of a career will help determine your lifestyle. As you read in Chapter 1, lifestyle is the way you use your time, energy, and resources. Your career will require much of your time and will also provide most of your financial resources. For example, someone who chooses to become a bank teller will have a regular workday with little overtime, thus leaving more time for family and leisure. Someone who chooses to become a doctor will have irregular hours, leaving less time for family and leisure, but will likely earn quite a lot more money than the bank teller. Your choice of a career should thus match how you want to spend your time and the financial resources you will need to support your lifestyle.

To help you learn about lifestyle, interview two workers—a male and a female—to find out how they feel about their lifestyles. A questionnaire is included in this activity to help you conduct the interviews. Use one copy of the questionnaire for your male worker and the other for the female worker. As you conduct each interview, write the respondent's answers to each question.

To begin your research, read the following information to each person you interview.

"A person's lifestyle is affected by several different things. Among the most important are the following five elements:

• Relationships with family
• Relationships with friends
• Leisure time
• Spiritual well-being, which may or may not be part of an organized faith
• Career

Think of these five elements of lifestyle as I ask you the following questions."

Bring your completed questionnaires to class for comparison and discussion. Try to discover whether people who are of similar ages or have similar careers also tend to have similar lifestyle views. Does a person's marital status or gender seem to affect attitude toward lifestyle and career?

Name _____ **Date** _____

Class _____ **Instructor** _____

Survey 1 Person's Career _____

      Age _____   **Marital Status** _____   **Gender** _____

1. Which part of your lifestyle—family, friends, leisure activities, spiritual well-being, or career—is most important to you? Why?

_____

_____

2. Which of the five parts—family, friends, leisure activities, spiritual well-being, or career—do you wish you could get greater satisfaction from than you do now?

_____

3. How does your career affect the other four parts of your lifestyle?

_____

_____

_____

4. What caused you to choose your present career?

_____

_____

5. How often have you changed careers? _____

Are you interested in changing careers in the future? Yes _____ No _____

6. Aside from the money you earn, what gives you a sense of satisfaction with your career?

_____

_____

7. What, if anything, could you have done in the past to make your work more satisfying today?

_____

_____

8. What advice do you have for me as I choose and prepare for a career?

_____

_____

_____

_____

Survey 2   Person's Career _____

        Age _____   **Marital Status** _____   **Gender** _____

1. Which part of your lifestyle—family, friends, leisure activities, spiritual well-being, or career—is most important to you? Why?

_____

_____

2. Which of the five parts—family, friends, leisure activities, spiritual well-being, or career—do you wish you could get greater satisfaction from than you do now?

_____

3. How does your career affect the other four parts of your lifestyle?

_____

_____

_____

4. What caused you to choose your present career?

_____

_____

5. How often have you changed careers? _____

Are you interested in changing careers in the future? Yes _____ No _____

6. Aside from the money you earn, what gives you a sense of satisfaction with your career?

_____

_____

7. What, if anything, could you have done in the past to make your work more satisfying today?

_____

_____

8. What advice do you have for me as I choose and prepare for a career?

_____

_____

_____

_____

_____

CHAPTER **1** You and the World of Work

ACTIVITY 1-2	**Foundation Skills**
Your Lifestyle Goals	*Thinking Skills: Creative Thinking*

Objective: To help you begin thinking about your personal lifestyle goals.

   In Activity 1-1 you interviewed two workers. You learned which of the five major parts of lifestyle were most important to each person. Use the information you gained from these surveys to start thinking about your own lifestyle goals.

   Look at the lifestyle pattern below. You can see from the sizes of the different parts that spiritual well-being and family are the most important parts of this person's lifestyle. Use the space provided below to draw your own lifestyle pattern as you hope it will be in ten years. On a separate sheet of paper, write a paragraph explaining why you drew some parts of your lifestyle larger than other parts.

Sample Lifestyle Pattern   **My Lifestyle Goal**

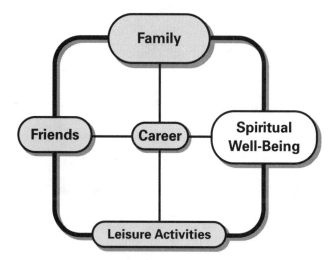

CHAPTER *1* You and the World of Work

ACTIVITY 1-3	**Foundation Skills**
Your Local Economic Outlook	*Thinking Skills:* *Knowing How to Learn*

Objective: To help you learn how to use different types of resources to gain information.

Your teacher will ask a representative of a local employment service or a member of your local Chamber of Commerce to visit your class. Ask for the facts needed to complete the following chart for a bulletin board display. Add other occupations if you wish. To learn more about your area's economic outlook, also find the answers to the questions following the chart.

Local Employment Survey					
		Number of Jobs in the Community **(check the appropriate column)**			
Type of Employment	**Salary Range**	**0–10**	**10–25**	**25–100**	**Over 100**
Architect					
Auto mechanic					
Barber					
Carpenter					
Computer programmer					
Construction worker					
Cook/chef					
Cosmetologist					
Dental lab technician					
Electrician					
Furniture upholsterer					
Librarian					
Nurse					
Painter					
Plumber					
Private household worker					
Shipping/receiving clerk					
Social worker					
Word processor					
Truck driver					
Waiter					
Welder					

1. a. Which type of work pays the most for an entry-level job? _____

_____

   b. Which pays the least? _____

_____

2. a. Which type of employment has the greatest number of jobs in this geographic area?

_____

_____

   b. Which has the fewest? _____

3. Choose one of the jobs from the list in which you might want to work. What is the average entry-level salary for a worker in that job?

_____

4. a. What is the rate of unemployment in this area? _____

   b. How does this rate compare with the national unemployment rate?

_____

5. Which jobs seem to offer the best opportunities in this area? Why?

_____

_____

_____

_____

6. Which companies are the top employers for this area?

_____

_____

_____

7. Have any companies recently gone out of business or moved away from this area? Why?

_____

_____

_____

_____

8. What new businesses have started up in this community or have relocated to the area?

_____

_____

_____

_____

_____

_____

9. How have living costs, incomes, taxes, and number of jobs changed in this area over the past two years?

_____

_____

_____

_____

_____

_____

10. Based on your research, what do you expect the area's economic situation to be five years from now?

_____

_____

_____

_____

_____

_____

CHAPTER **1** You and the World of Work

ACTIVITY 1-4
Surveying Another Community's Economy

Workplace Competencies

*Information:
Acquiring and Evaluating Information*

Objective: To investigate the economic conditions of another community.

When you are considering moving to another community to obtain employment, it is a good idea to discover what the economy is like there. One way you can do this is by writing to the town's Chamber of Commerce. For this activity, you will write to the Chamber of Commerce of another community to investigate the economic conditions of their town.

First, choose a town you would like to learn more about. Next, obtain the address of the Chamber of Commerce for the town. You can get this address from your local Chamber of Commerce or from references in your local public library. If you have Internet access, you may also be able to find a home page for the city of interest.

Using the next page, write a rough copy of your letter. The parts of a business letter are identified in parentheses. If you need help in writing a business letter, refer to reference manuals or books on business communications. In your letter, request information about the community's economic outlook and ask them to send you brochures about their area. You may want to ask some of the same questions used in Activity 1-3.

Revise your letter. If you have access to a computer, use a word-processing program to produce your finished letter. Be sure to use appropriate format and check your letter for incorrect grammar and misspellings. Print out a finished copy and mail the letter. After you have received your reply, review the materials sent and decide on the advantages and disadvantages of the community. Share your information with the class, giving your opinion on whether the community would be a good place to search for employment.

_____ _(Date)_

_____ _(Inside Address)_

_____

_____

_____

_____ _(Salutation)_

(Body of letter—usually three to four paragraphs)

_____

_____

_____

_____

_____

_____

_____

_____

_____

_____

_____

_____

_____

_____

_____ _(Complimentary close)_

_____ _(Your name)_

CHAPTER 1 You and the World of Work

ACTIVITY 1-5	**Research**
Employment Trends	

Objective: To gather information on the current and future national job market.

As you know from your reading, people who can adapt to changes in the workplace are more likely to gain financial security than those who have limited themselves to a job with shrinking opportunities. When you researched careers, you may have rejected some careers because their job outlooks were not good. For this activity, you are to research the latest national employment trends. Use the *Occupational Outlook Handbook* and other library or Internet resources.

In your research, discover which areas of the country are considered growth areas, what jobs are glutted or being phased out, and what jobs are predicted to grow during the next ten years. Then, in the space below, write a conclusion about the kinds of careers high school students should prepare for to give themselves a greater chance of financial security.

1. Conclusion

_____

_____

_____

_____

2. Sources Used

_____

_____

3. What are some actions you could take based on your conclusion and research?

_____

_____

_____

CHAPTER 2 Getting to Know Yourself

ACTIVITY 2-1	Foundation Skills
Identifying Your Values	*Personal Qualities: Self-Management*

Objective: To help you identify your values and to determine how your personal values affect your career choices.

As you know from reading Chapter 2, values are the principles that you want to live by and the beliefs that are important to you. You need to know what your values are so that you can better select a career that fits with those values. Otherwise, you might choose a career that conflicts with your values.

Below and on the next few pages are 100 statements that deal with ten types of values. Read each statement carefully. Then rate the statement as it applies to you.

If the statement is *definitely true* for you, circle 10.
If the statement is *mostly true* for you, circle 7.
If you are *undecided* about whether the statement applies to you, circle 5.
If the statement is *mostly false* for you, circle 3.
If the statement is *definitely false* for you, circle 0.

Value Statements	Definitely True	Mostly True	Undecided	Mostly False	Definitely False
1. I have a physical checkup every year.	10	7	5	3	0
2. What people think of me is more important than the amount of money I have.	10	7	5	3	0
3. I enjoy attending musical concerts.	10	7	5	3	0
4. It is important to me to have many friends.	10	7	5	3	0
5. I donate to charities that I feel are worthwhile.	10	7	5	3	0
6. I envy the way movie stars are recognized wherever they go.	10	7	5	3	0
7. I would like to have enough money to retire at 50.	10	7	5	3	0
8. I would rather spend an evening at home with my family than go out with friends.	10	7	5	3	0
9. I enjoy making decisions that involve other people.	10	7	5	3	0
10. If I had the talent, I would like to write songs.	10	7	5	3	0
11. I have a close relationship with at least one of my parents.	10	7	5	3	0
12. I would report a relative who committed a crime.	10	7	5	3	0

(Continued on next page)

	Definitely True	Mostly True	Undecided	Mostly False	Definitely False
13. I am willing to spend time helping fellow students who are having difficulty with their studies.	10	7	5	3	0
14. Even if earning the same salary, I would rather be the boss than just another worker.	10	7	5	3	0
15. I have a special appreciation for beautiful things.	10	7	5	3	0
16. If I had the talent, I would like to appear regularly on television.	10	7	5	3	0
17. I would like to counsel people and help them with their problems.	10	7	5	3	0
18. I would enjoy associating with movie stars and other celebrities.	10	7	5	3	0
19. I have a dental checkup at least once a year.	10	7	5	3	0
20. I enjoy writing short stories.	10	7	5	3	0
21. I would rather spend a summer working than going on a paid vacation.	10	7	5	3	0
22. I like to go to parties.	10	7	5	3	0
23. I think it would be fun to write a play for television.	10	7	5	3	0
24. I would voice my beliefs even if they were unpopular with others.	10	7	5	3	0
25. I would rather be an officer than just a club member.	10	7	5	3	0
26. I would rather spend my last $100 for needed dental work than for a vacation at a favorite amusement park.	10	7	5	3	0
27. I enjoy giving presents to members of my family.	10	7	5	3	0
28. If I were a teacher, I would rather teach poetry than math.	10	7	5	3	0
29. I often have daydreams about things that I would do if I had the money.	10	7	5	3	0
30. I enjoy giving parties.	10	7	5	3	0
31. I am willing to write letters for people who are unable to write their own, such as elderly or ill persons.	10	7	5	3	0
32. It would be very satisfying to receive publicity for acting in movies or television.	10	7	5	3	0
33. When I feel ill, I usually go to the doctor.	10	7	5	3	0
34. I would tell the truth even if it hurt a friend.	10	7	5	3	0
35. I enjoy taking part in discussions at the family dinner table.	10	7	5	3	0
36. I enjoy visiting art museums.	10	7	5	3	0
37. I like to write poetry.	10	7	5	3	0
38. I like to be around other people most of the time.	10	7	5	3	0
39. I like to be the one who decides what we will do or where we will go when I'm out with friends.	10	7	5	3	0
40. Someday I would like to live in a large, expensive house.	10	7	5	3	0
41. Each day I try to set aside some time for worship.	10	7	5	3	0
42. If I knew a family that had no food for a holiday dinner, I would try to provide it.	10	7	5	3	0
43. I like to spend holidays with my family.	10	7	5	3	0
44. I like to see my name in print (in the newspaper).	10	7	5	3	0
45. I would rather take a class in freehand drawing than a class in math.	10	7	5	3	0

	Definitely True	Mostly True	Undecided	Mostly False	Definitely False
46. I do not like to spend an entire evening alone.	10	7	5	3	0
47. If the salary were the same, I would rather be a school principal than a classroom teacher.	10	7	5	3	0
48. I have expensive tastes.	10	7	5	3	0
49. I can tell the difference between a really fine painting or drawing and an ordinary one.	10	7	5	3	0
50. If I had regular headaches, I would consult a doctor even if aspirin or other over-the-counter medications lessened the pain.	10	7	5	3	0
51. I have several very close friends.	10	7	5	3	0
52. I expect to provide music lessons for my children.	10	7	5	3	0
53. I always respect other people's beliefs, both religious and personal.	10	7	5	3	0
54. I sometimes miss sleep to visit late with friends.	10	7	5	3	0
55. I usually get at least eight hours of sleep each night.	10	7	5	3	0
56. I like to design things.	10	7	5	3	0
57. I would rather be well known throughout the country than highly respected by my coworkers.	10	7	5	3	0
58. I would get a sense of satisfaction from nursing a sick person back to health.	10	7	5	3	0
59. I care what my parents think about the things I do.	10	7	5	3	0
60. I daydream about making a great deal of money.	10	7	5	3	0
61. I like to be the chairperson at meetings.	10	7	5	3	0
62. It is thrilling to come up with an original idea and put it to use.	10	7	5	3	0
63. I would not do work that I thought to be unethical under any circumstances.	10	7	5	3	0
64. If someone is hard to get along with, I try to be understanding.	10	7	5	3	0
65. If I were in the television field, I would rather be a celebrated actor than a scriptwriter.	10	7	5	3	0
66. I enjoy decorating my room at home.	10	7	5	3	0
67. I enjoy a picnic with my family.	10	7	5	3	0
68. As an adult, I want to earn a much higher salary than the average worker.	10	7	5	3	0
69. I am careful to eat a balanced diet each day.	10	7	5	3	0
70. I often influence other students concerning the classes they take.	10	7	5	3	0
71. I would like to be written up in *Who's Who*.	10	7	5	3	0
72. I always stand up for my beliefs.	10	7	5	3	0
73. If I were in the clothing industry, I would enjoy creating new styles.	10	7	5	3	0
74. I look forward to an evening out with a group of friends.	10	7	5	3	0
75. When I am with a group of people, I like to be the one in charge.	10	7	5	3	0
76. I dislike being financially dependent on others.	10	7	5	3	0
77. I feel I must comfort a friend who is in trouble.	10	7	5	3	0

(Continued on next page)

		Definitely True	Mostly True	Undecided	Mostly False	Definitely False
78.	I love my parents.	10	7	5	3	0
79.	I almost never skip meals.	10	7	5	3	0
80.	I have a collection of music CDs.	10	7	5	3	0
81.	I have a particular friend with whom I discuss problems.	10	7	5	3	0
82.	I believe it is important to support my religion by giving my time and/or money.	10	7	5	3	0
83.	I enjoy buying clothes for members of my family.	10	7	5	3	0
84.	I would enjoy having people recognize me wherever I go.	10	7	5	3	0
85.	I like planning activities for others.	10	7	5	3	0
86.	I do not smoke.	10	7	5	3	0
87.	I feel good when I do things that help others.	10	7	5	3	0
88.	Someday I would like to write a novel.	10	7	5	3	0
89.	I would put up with undesirable living conditions in order to work at a job that paid extremely well.	10	7	5	3	0
90.	I belong to several clubs and organizations.	10	7	5	3	0
91.	I would turn in a friend who did something illegal.	10	7	5	3	0
92.	I would enjoy having my picture in the school yearbook more than it has been in the past.	10	7	5	3	0
93.	I often organize group activities.	10	7	5	3	0
94.	When I see a newly constructed building, I consider its beauty as much as its practical use.	10	7	5	3	0
95.	I respect my father and mother.	10	7	5	3	0
96.	I like to design or make things that have not been made before.	10	7	5	3	0
97.	Some of the hobbies I would like to have are quite expensive.	10	7	5	3	0
98.	I enjoy classical music.	10	7	5	3	0
99.	I would never use potentially harmful drugs because of what they might do to my body.	10	7	5	3	0
100.	I am kind to animals.	10	7	5	3	0

The numbers of the 100 statements that you just rated are listed under the appropriate values in the chart below. For example, statements 6, 16, 18, 32, and so on all relate to the value *fame;* therefore, they are listed under *Fame.* To determine your rating for each value, write the number that you circled (10, 7, 5, 3, or 0) for each statement on the blank next to the statement number. Then add the numbers in each column to get your total for each value.

Value Ratings Chart

Fame	Money	Power	Ethics/Religion	Humanitarianism
6. _____	7. _____	9. _____	2. _____	5. _____
16. _____	21. _____	14. _____	12. _____	13. _____
18. _____	29. _____	25. _____	24. _____	17. _____
32. _____	40. _____	39. _____	34. _____	31. _____
44. _____	48. _____	47. _____	41. _____	42. _____
57. _____	60. _____	61. _____	53. _____	58. _____
65. _____	68. _____	70. _____	63. _____	64. _____
71. _____	76. _____	75. _____	72. _____	77. _____
84. _____	89. _____	85. _____	82. _____	87. _____
92. _____	97. _____	93. _____	91. _____	100. _____
Total ☐	Total ☐	Total ☐	Total ☐	Total ☐

Family	Health	Aesthetics	Creativity	Social Contact
8. _____	1. _____	3. _____	10. _____	4. _____
11. _____	19. _____	15. _____	20. _____	22. _____
27. _____	26. _____	28. _____	23. _____	30. _____
35. _____	33. _____	36. _____	37. _____	38. _____
43. _____	50. _____	49. _____	45. _____	46. _____
59. _____	55. _____	52. _____	56. _____	51. _____
67. _____	69. _____	66. _____	62. _____	54. _____
78. _____	79. _____	80. _____	73. _____	74. _____
83. _____	86. _____	94. _____	88. _____	81. _____
95. _____	99. _____	98. _____	96. _____	90. _____
Total ☐	Total ☐	Total ☐	Total ☐	Total ☐

(Continued on next page)

Use the graph below to chart your ratings for each of the ten values. The peaks will show the values that are most important to you. The graph already shows the average ratings for each of the ten values for males and females. The averages are based on the ratings of students from junior and senior high school across the country. After plotting your own ratings, you will see how your values compare with those of other students your age.

Value Ratings

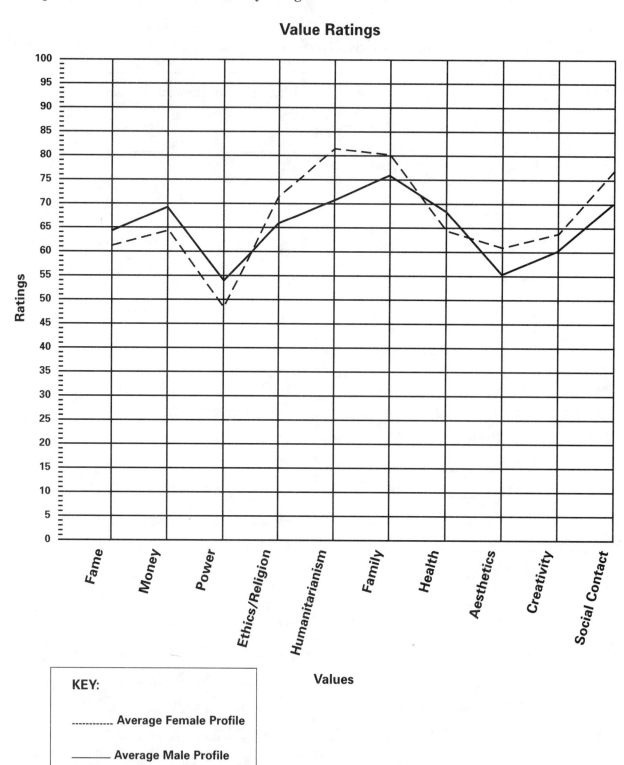

KEY:

--------- Average Female Profile

————— Average Male Profile

CHAPTER 2 Getting to Know Yourself

ACTIVITY 2-2	**Foundation Skills**
What Are Your Interests?	*Personal Qualities: Self-Management*

Objective: To help you identify personal interests that could lead to a career choice.

One way of getting to know yourself better is to examine your interests. Use the list below to rate the hobbies and leisure activities that you find interesting. Write in any of your interests that are not listed. Use the following scale to rate each interest.

5 = extremely interesting   **3** = fairly interesting   **0** = not interesting
4 = very interesting   **2** = slightly interesting

_____ Animals	_____ Crafts	_____ Reading
_____ Art	_____ Dancing	_____ Religious activities
_____ Astronomy	_____ Debates or public speaking	_____ Running
_____ Backpacking or hiking	_____ Films	_____ Sailing
_____ Ballet or opera	_____ Fishing	_____ Science projects
_____ Baseball	_____ Flying	_____ Sewing
_____ Basketball	_____ Football	_____ Snow skiing
_____ Biking	_____ Gardening	_____ Softball
_____ Billiards	_____ Golf	_____ Spectator sports
_____ Bowling	_____ Gymnastics	_____ Sports cars
_____ Bridge	_____ Skating	_____ Stamp collecting
_____ Building models	_____ Magic	_____ Swimming
_____ Camping	_____ Music	_____ Tennis
_____ Canoeing	_____ Painting	_____ Travel
_____ Ceramics	_____ Parties	_____ Volleyball
_____ Chess	_____ Photography	_____ Volunteer work
_____ Child care	_____ Picnics	_____ Water skiing
_____ Coin collecting	_____ Plays or concerts	_____ Wrestling
_____ Computer games	_____ Political activities	_____ Writing
_____ Cooking	_____ Rafting	_____ Woodworking

Now look at your ratings. Of the interests you rated 4 or 5, which are your three favorites?

_____   _____   _____
First Choice   Second Choice   Third Choice

CHAPTER 2 Getting to Know Yourself

ACTIVITY 2-3	**Foundation Skills**
Vocabulary Aptitude Test	*Basic Skills: Reading*

Objective: To help you determine how well your vocabulary compares with the vocabularies of students throughout the country.

Some people have better verbal skills, while others are better in mathematics or are more artistic. For those with a high level of verbal skills, a career as a novelist or a journalist might be appealing. Many employers today give tests such as this to determine whether a job applicant's verbal skills are equal to the requirements of the job. This vocabulary test will help give you a better idea of your verbal aptitude and whether you need to work on improving your skills.

This test measures how well you understand the meanings of words. In the left-hand column below and on the following pages are 100 words. Read each word at the left, then the list of words that follow. Fill in the box in front of the word or phrase that is the best meaning of the word at the left. Look at the following example.

attain ☐ climb ☐ achieve ☐ possess ☐ defer

The best definition is *achieve*, so you would fill in the box in front of *achieve*.

You are allowed exactly ten minutes for this test. You may time yourself or have someone else time you. Do not look at the words before you start. Do not take longer than ten minutes. Otherwise, you will not be able to compare your vocabulary skills with those of other students who have taken the test. Begin when you are ready.

1. panic ☐ decorate ☐ cluster ☐ sudden fear ☐ puffing sound
2. haste ☐ linger ☐ unhurried ☐ speed ☐ wasteful
3. combine ☐ activate ☐ blend ☐ harness ☐ stack
4. participate ☐ begin ☐ create ☐ take part ☐ lead
5. litter ☐ unit of measure ☐ untidy rubbish ☐ unimportant ☐ limited importance
6. slumber ☐ shuffle ☐ sleep ☐ recline ☐ ignore
7. refrain ☐ abstain ☐ react ☐ respect ☐ heed
8. equip ☐ supplies ☐ prepare ☐ assist ☐ pack
9. persist ☐ infectious ☐ obstinate ☐ continue ☐ prevail
10. luscious ☐ delicious ☐ desperate ☐ excited ☐ drunk
11. distribute ☐ excel ☐ dispense ☐ cast ☐ flow
12. exhale ☐ display ☐ breathe out ☐ unfold ☐ refresh
13. novice ☐ officer ☐ beginner ☐ expert ☐ religious leader
14. blemish ☐ polish ☐ whiten ☐ mix ☐ defect
15. violation ☐ infringement ☐ celebration ☐ concert ☐ excitement

16. midst ☐ middle ☐ rain ☐ haze ☐ film

17. abandon ☐ surround ☐ subside ☐ restrain ☐ desert

18. compel ☐ force ☐ match ☐ reject ☐ destroy

19. humble ☐ angry ☐ sloppy ☐ greedy ☐ meek

20. lineage ☐ pipeline ☐ ancestry ☐ young ☐ timeless

21. anonymous ☐ amorphous ☐ quiet ☐ tiresome ☐ unnamed

22. addiction ☐ adhere ☐ dissertation ☐ compulsion ☐ adamant

23. initiate ☐ begin ☐ request ☐ act in innocence ☐ hesitate

24. compatible ☐ accountable ☐ capable of existing harmoniously ☐ ability to stir to action ☐ permanent

25. erroneous ☐ unfair ☐ silly ☐ dishonest ☐ mistaken

26. random ☐ haphazard ☐ rancid ☐ widespread ☐ incomplete

27. quest ☐ veer ☐ search ☐ ask ☐ study

28. elite ☐ precise ☐ delicate ☐ speed ☐ superior

29. prevail ☐ avert ☐ triumph ☐ prevent ☐ seize

30. deplete ☐ deploy ☐ exhaust or lessen ☐ refill ☐ worn

31. remunerate ☐ arbitrate ☐ advise ☐ pay ☐ release

32. compilation ☐ material gathered from various sources ☐ deep thought ☐ to bring to an end ☐ a heap

33. variable ☐ cloudy ☐ changeable ☐ unapproachable ☐ unavoidable

34. terrain ☐ area of land ☐ boundary ☐ article of clothing ☐ creek bed

35. meager ☐ plentiful ☐ meek ☐ scanty ☐ submissive

36. comprehensive ☐ easily understood ☐ to combine ☐ believable ☐ wide in scope

37. compassionate ☐ excitable ☐ sympathetic ☐ emotionally upset ☐ religious

38. manipulate ☐ control ☐ to build ☐ to hinder ☐ exercise

39. precede ☐ prefer ☐ go before ☐ acquire beforehand ☐ to climb

40. category ☐ direct statement ☐ mandate ☐ class or division ☐ political address

41. retroactive ☐ decreasing ☐ becoming inactive ☐ explosive ☐ effective at prior time

42. chaos ☐ violence ☐ extreme disorder ☐ military rule ☐ misunderstanding

43. digress ☐ turn aside ☐ weaken ☐ take apart ☐ give up

44. minimal ☐ microscopic ☐ least possible ☐ infinite ☐ median

45. unprecedented ☐ dissimilar ☐ improbable ☐ never occurred before ☐ unacclaimed

46. cohesion ☐ sticking together ☐ body growth ☐ to force ☐ a fissure

47. conscientious ☐ aware ☐ orderly ☐ scrupulous ☐ thoughtful

48. validate ☐ appraise ☐ confirm ☐ nullify ☐ improve

49. delete ☐ add ☐ reverse ☐ erase ☐ weaken

50. myopic ☐ nearsighted ☐ old ☐ stupid ☐ nervous

51. provocation ☐ a proposal ☐ prophetic ☐ a declaration ☐ a cause of anger

52. ostentatious ☐ loud ☐ showy ☐ big ☐ wealthy

53. retaliatory ☐ repetitive ☐ forceful ☐ anxious ☐ revengeful

54. dullard ☐ a type of bird ☐ a clumsy person ☐ a stupid person ☐ a lazy person

(Continued on next page)

55. impudent ☐ cute ☐ rude ☐ unfair ☐ devious

56. disrupt ☐ destroy ☐ throw into disorder ☐ break into ☐ eruption

57. pursuant ☐ persuasive ☐ to chase ☐ at great speed ☐ in accordance with

58. forestall ☐ prevent by prior action ☐ a legal procedure ☐ to force against one's will ☐ to anticipate

59. manifold ☐ a large enclosure ☐ many and varied ☐ a pressing machine ☐ a listing of cargo

60. nullify ☐ to make permanent ☐ to make insensitive ☐ to deprive of effect ☐ ridicule

61. demise ☐ death ☐ discouragement ☐ lack of attention ☐ infatuation

62. thwart ☐ arouse ☐ displease ☐ convince ☐ prevent

63. relinquish ☐ brighten ☐ long for ☐ let go ☐ destroy

64. apathy ☐ illness ☐ shyness ☐ disagreeable ☐ indifference

65. unilateral ☐ affecting one side only ☐ a form with parallel lines ☐ international law ☐ one side of a triangle

66. envision ☐ hope for ☐ make plans for ☐ surround ☐ foresee in imagination

67. manifest ☐ obscure ☐ obvious ☐ individualized ☐ appropriate

68. congeal ☐ to flow ☐ to thicken ☐ to adhere ☐ to stretch

69. accrue ☐ earn ☐ record ☐ accumulate ☐ fasten

70. disseminate ☐ an incision ☐ to spread widely ☐ separate ☐ banish

71. repudiate ☐ answer back ☐ reject ☐ revise ☐ reform

72. sanctuary ☐ refuge ☐ religious ceremony ☐ freedom ☐ forgiveness

73. sustenance ☐ encouragement ☐ vitality ☐ nourishment ☐ guidance

74. inopportune ☐ nuisance ☐ awkward ☐ unnatural ☐ untimely

75. sparsity ☐ stinginess ☐ scarcity ☐ widespread ☐ dense

76. encompass ☐ to direct ☐ to surround ☐ engage in conflict ☐ to hinder

77. obsolescence ☐ old ☐ to keep watch ☐ stubbornly defiant ☐ falling into disuse

78. implicate ☐ pardon ☐ involve ☐ to bring suit against ☐ absolute

79. renovate ☐ to restore ☐ to recall a nostalgic experience ☐ to change location ☐ to imitate

80. pliant ☐ to braid ☐ twisted ☐ flexible ☐ importune

81. subterfuge ☐ to seize ☐ a tunnel ☐ imply ☐ trick

82. decibel ☐ monetary unit ☐ one in a group of ten ☐ that which destroys ☐ measure of sound

83. cataclysmic ☐ inducing action ☐ disastrous ☐ subterranean burial ☐ clouding of the lens of the eye

84. abate ☐ decrease ☐ increase ☐ tease ☐ triumph

85. plaudit ☐ apparent truth ☐ commonplace ☐ resistant ☐ enthusiastic approval

86. contingent ☐ adjoining ☐ scornful ☐ satisfied ☐ dependent

87. ludicrous ☐ unclear ☐ profitable ☐ laughable ☐ awkward

88. meticulous ☐ tiny ☐ precise ☐ type of measurement ☐ type of organism

89. reciprocity ☐ mutual cooperation ☐ incline backwards ☐ adjust ☐ to deliver

90. ponderous ☐ thoughtful ☐ heavy ☐ uncompromising ☐ complicated

91. obviate ☐ easily discovered ☐ overlap ☐ object ☐ make unnecessary

92. impropriety ☐ intolerant ☐ improper act ☐ ownership ☐ obstruction

93. subjugate   ☐ raise to a higher level ☐ to conquer ☐ compromise ☐ omit

94. portent   ☐ forewarning ☐ dowry ☐ depict ☐ strength

95. taciturn   ☐ lazy ☐ silent ☐ diplomatic ☐ relating to sense of touch

96. retentive   ☐ in seclusion ☐ secretive ☐ retaliatory ☐ not forgetful

97. replete   ☐ forgiven ☐ grumpy ☐ filled to the utmost ☐ rejected

98. accede   ☐ yield ☐ climb ☐ refuse ☐ beg

99. qualm   ☐ a measure of quantity ☐ peace ☐ responsibility ☐ sudden misgiving or fear

100. forbear   ☐ refrain ☐ attack ☐ oppose ☐ estimate

When you have finished the test, give it to your counselor or teacher to score. When you know your score, circle it below. You can then look directly across to the next column on the right to compare your score with the scores of students who have already taken the test. The numbers in this column are the percentages of students who scored *lower* than a particular score. For example, if you scored 56, you can see that 86 percent of the students scored lower than you. This would mean that your vocabulary is very good compared to the vocabularies of other students.

Score	Percentile	Score	Percentile	Score	Percentile
65+	95+	48	68	30	25
64	94	47	65	29	24
63	93	46	63	28	23
62	92	45	60	27	21
61	91	44	58	26	20
60	90	43	55	25	19
59	89	42	50	24	18
58	88	41	45	23	16
57	87	40	43	22	15
56	86	39	40	21	14
55	85	38	38	20	13
54	83	37	35	19	12
53	80	36	34	18	10
52	78	35	32	17	9
51	75	34	30	16	8
50	73	33	29	15	7
49	70	32	28	14	5
		31	26		

CHAPTER 2   Getting to Know Yourself

ACTIVITY 2-4	**Foundation Skills**
Math Aptitude Test	*Basic Skills:* *Mathematics*

Objective: To help you compare your math abilities with those of students around the country.

This test measures your math ability and aptitude. Employers whose jobs require the use of math often give such tests to entry-level applicants to determine the level of their math skills. If you want to work in a career that requires the application of math skills, this test will help you determine whether you need to improve those skills.

Following are 64 math problems. The first problems are relatively simple. The problems become more difficult as you work through the test. You can use scrap paper to work out your answers. *(Do not use a calculator.)* Fill in the box next to each correct answer as shown in the examples below.

Example 1

$$\begin{array}{r} 6 \\ +2 \\ \hline \end{array}$$

Answers

- ☐ 7
- ☐ 8
- ☐ 9
- ☐ 6
- ☐ none of these

Example 2

$$\begin{array}{r} 7 \\ -3 \\ \hline \end{array}$$

Answers

- ☐ 2
- ☐ 5
- ☐ 6
- ☐ 3
- ☐ none of these

Notice in the second example that the correct answer does not appear in the list of possible answers. In such a case, fill in the box next to *none of these*.

You are allowed 15 minutes for this test. You may time yourself or have someone else time you. Do not look at the problems before you start the test. Do not take any more than the allotted 15 minutes. Otherwise, you will not be able to accurately compare your results with those of other students who have taken the test. You may begin when you are ready.

1.
$$\begin{array}{r} 7 \\ +4 \\ \hline \end{array}$$

Answers

- ☐ 3
- ☐ 10
- ☐ 11
- ☐ 12
- ☐ none of these

2.
$$\begin{array}{r} 8 \\ -3 \\ \hline \end{array}$$

- ☐ 4
- ☐ 5
- ☐ 10
- ☐ 11
- ☐ none of these

3.
$$\begin{array}{r} 7 \\ \times 3 \\ \hline \end{array}$$

Answers

- ☐ 4
- ☐ 10
- ☐ 21
- ☐ 28
- ☐ none of these

4. $3\overline{)24}$

- ☐ 6
- ☐ 7
- ☐ 8
- ☐ 9
- ☐ none of these

Answers   **Answers**

5. 8
    7
  +4
☐ 15
☐ 16
☐ 17
☐ 18
☐ none of these

14. 97
   −16
☐ 71
☐ 79
☐ 81
☐ 83
☐ none of these

6. 23
   −4
☐ 19
☐ 21
☐ 24
☐ 27
☐ none of these

15. 35
   ×12
☐ 410
☐ 420
☐ 430
☐ 440
☐ none of these

7. 11
   ×4
☐ 41
☐ 44
☐ 48
☐ 49
☐ none of these

16. 7)1302
☐ 176
☐ 184
☐ 186
☐ 196
☐ none of these

8. 5)125
☐ 15
☐ 21
☐ 25
☐ 30
☐ none of these

17. 42
    16
  +12
☐ 60
☐ 70
☐ 80
☐ 90
☐ none of these

9. 32
  +16
☐ 46
☐ 47
☐ 48
☐ 49
☐ none of these

18. 92
   −18
☐ 70
☐ 74
☐ 80
☐ 84
☐ none of these

10. 85
   −32
☐ 51
☐ 53
☐ 55
☐ 57
☐ none of these

19. 43
   ×14
☐ 502
☐ 602
☐ 612
☐ 672
☐ none of these

11. 135
    ×6
☐ 141
☐ 685
☐ 695
☐ 810
☐ none of these

20. 6)1140
☐ 140
☐ 160
☐ 190
☐ 240
☐ none of these

12. 8)1096
☐ 137
☐ 139
☐ 143
☐ 156
☐ none of these

21. 18
    34
  +62
☐ 112
☐ 113
☐ 114
☐ 115
☐ none of these

13. 75
  +23
☐ 97
☐ 98
☐ 99
☐ 108
☐ none of these

22. 87
   −19
☐ 66
☐ 68
☐ 76
☐ 78
☐ none of these

(Continued on next page)

Answers   **Answers**

23.   56   ☐ 905   **32.** 12)3000   ☐ 250
          ×18   ☐ 906   ☐ 275
                       ☐ 907   ☐ 300
                       ☐ 908   ☐ 325
                       ☐ none of these   ☐ none of these

24. 7)1491   ☐ 213   **33.**   315   ☐ 641
                       ☐ 223   121   ☐ 649
                       ☐ 233   +215   ☐ 652
                       ☐ 243   ☐ 659
                       ☐ none of these   ☐ none of these

25. 7% × 200   ☐ 13   **34.** 1567   ☐ 1479
                       ☐ 14   −88   ☐ 1489
                       ☐ 1.4   ☐ 1499
                       ☐ 14.0   ☐ 1509
                       ☐ none of these   ☐ none of these

26.   74   ☐ 14   **35.** 12% of 760   ☐ 91.2
          −57   ☐ 17   ☐ 912
                       ☐ 24   ☐ 63.3
                       ☐ 27   ☐ 9120
                       ☐ none of these   ☐ none of these

27.   85   ☐ 1685   **36.** 12)4740   ☐ 355
          ×21   ☐ 1785   ☐ 365
                       ☐ 1865   ☐ 375
                       ☐ 1885   ☐ 385
                       ☐ none of these   ☐ none of these

28. 9)2025   ☐ 215   **37.**   853   ☐ 2464
                       ☐ 225   590   ☐ 2524
                       ☐ 275   264   ☐ 2544
                       ☐ 295   +857   ☐ 2564
                       ☐ none of these   ☐ none of these

29.   18   ☐ 82   **38.** 2318   ☐ 1809
           19   ☐ 83   −499   ☐ 1819
           23   ☐ 92   ☐ 1829
            6   ☐ 93   ☐ 1839
           14   ☐ none of these   ☐ none of these
          +12
                                      39. 5% × 1840   ☐ 368
30. 518   ☐ 379   ☐ 90
         −39   ☐ 389   ☐ 36800
                       ☐ 399   ☐ 920
                       ☐ 479   ☐ none of these
                       ☐ none of these
                                      40. 8)5144   ☐ 543
31. 110   ☐ 1310   ☐ 633
         ×12   ☐ 1320   ☐ 643
                       ☐ 1340   ☐ 653
                       ☐ 1360   ☐ none of these
                       ☐ none of these

Answers   **Answers**

41.
```
  1864
  1375
+2387
```
☐ 5626
☐ 5636
☐ 5646
☐ 5656
☐ none of these

42.
```
  4618
−1935
```
☐ 2663
☐ 2673
☐ 2683
☐ 2693
☐ none of these

43.
```
 714
×35
```
☐ 2499
☐ 24790
☐ 24890
☐ 24990
☐ none of these

44. 12)4788
☐ 369
☐ 379
☐ 389
☐ 399
☐ none of these

45.
```
 4260
×.08
```
☐ 340.8
☐ 3408
☐ 5325
☐ 5335
☐ none of these

46.
```
  7533
−6438
```
☐ 1065
☐ 1075
☐ 1085
☐ 1095
☐ none of these

47.
```
 514
×44
```
☐ 21516
☐ 22616
☐ 22936
☐ 23536
☐ none of these

48. 15)7575
☐ 505
☐ 515
☐ 525
☐ 555
☐ none of these

49.
```
 753
 783
 648
 253
+532
```
☐ 2939
☐ 2959
☐ 2979
☐ 2999
☐ none of these

50.
```
 8545
×.12
```
☐ 102.54
☐ 1025.4
☐ 102540
☐ 10.254
☐ none of these

51.
```
 683
×46
```
☐ 31418
☐ 32818
☐ 32838
☐ 32848
☐ none of these

52. 36)30024
☐ 834
☐ 844
☐ 854
☐ 864
☐ none of these

53.
```
 358
 643
 658
 347
 453
+542
```
☐ 2991
☐ 2999
☐ 3001
☐ 3002
☐ none of these

54.
```
  7543
−7289
```
☐ 244
☐ 249
☐ 254
☐ 259
☐ none of these

55.
```
 789
×39
```
☐ 30731
☐ 30751
☐ 30771
☐ 30791
☐ none of these

56. 43)37840
☐ 88
☐ 880
☐ 888
☐ 898
☐ none of these

57.
```
 654
 347
 753
 432
 767
+422
```
☐ 3275
☐ 3325
☐ 3355
☐ 3375
☐ none of these

58.
```
  9865
−1798
```
☐ 8067
☐ 8077
☐ 8167
☐ 8177
☐ none of these

(Continued on next page)

		Answers				**Answers**

59.   789
     ×68

- ☐ 53553
- ☐ 53562
- ☐ 53662
- ☐ 53682
- ☐ none of these

62.   5435
     −4356

- ☐ 1059
- ☐ 1069
- ☐ 1079
- ☐ 1089
- ☐ none of these

60. 85)66725

- ☐ 755
- ☐ 765
- ☐ 785
- ☐ 795
- ☐ none of these

63.   893
     ×46

- ☐ 40078
- ☐ 41078
- ☐ 41178
- ☐ 41088
- ☐ none of these

61. 25% of 7000

- ☐ 28000
- ☐ 1780
- ☐ 1750
- ☐ 17500
- ☐ none of these

64. 62)48670

- ☐ 735
- ☐ 755
- ☐ 775
- ☐ 785
- ☐ none of these

When you have finished the test, give it to your counselor or teacher to score. When you know your score, circle it below. To compare your score with the scores of other students, look directly across from your score to the next column on the right. The number in this column tells the percentage of students who scored lower than you on the test. For example, if you scored 37, 50 percent of the students scored higher and 50 percent scored lower. This score means that you currently have average math skills. If you are interested in a career that requires better math skills, you can improve your skills through study and practice.

Score	Percentile	Score	Percentile
55+	99+	36	45
54	98	35	40
53	97	34	35
52	96	33	30
51	95	32	26
50	94	31	23
49	93	30	20
48	91	29	17
47	89	28	14
46	86	27	11
45	83	26	9
44	80	25	7
43	77	24	6
42	74	23	5
41	70	22	4
40	65	21	3
39	60	20	2
38	55	19	1
37	50		

CHAPTER **2** Getting to Know Yourself

ACTIVITY 2-5	**Foundation Skills**
Consider Your Personality	*Thinking Skills:* *Seeing Things in the Mind's Eye*

Objective: To help you learn more about yourself so that you will be able to match your personality traits with a career in which those traits will help you be successful.

The picture you have of yourself in your mind gives important clues about your personality. When you have a clear perception of the kind of person you are, you can more easily find a career that will suit you. By learning about your general personality type, you can discover how you are likely to behave in your career. Knowing your personality strengths and weaknesses will help you to choose a career that takes advantage of your strengths while downplaying your weaknesses.

1. List 12 words that describe the kind of person you are.

_____ _____ _____

_____ _____ _____

_____ _____ _____

_____ _____ _____

2. List 12 words that describe the kind of person you are not.

_____ _____ _____

_____ _____ _____

_____ _____ _____

_____ _____ _____

(Continued on next page)

3. Read the words in each column below, then circle 16 words that you believe describe you. Total the number of words circled in each column.

Column 1	Column 2	Column 3	Column 4
bright	outgoing	predictable	mathematical
decisive	emotional	team player	precise
independent	cooperative	calm	cautious
competitive	friendly	thorough	intellectual
direct	helpful	self-composed	curious
adventurous	idealistic	persistent	controlling
aggressive	trusting	loyal	systematic
ambitious	self-assured	supportive	precise
self-confident	influencing	conforming	accurate
assertive	spontaneous	obedient	conventional
Total:_____	Total:_____	Total:_____	Total:_____

The column in which you have the most words circled describes how you see your own personality. Write the number of that column in this space. _____

Now read about the personality types and see whether the description is accurate for you.

1. **Dominant Personality:** People who have dominant personalities want to be in control of their environment. They are good at setting goals and focusing on the work needed to accomplish goals. Dominant personalities like being in positions of leadership and usually seek careers that give them some control over their work, such as managers, business owners, and lawyers.

2. **Influencing Personality:** People who are influencers like to work in careers that allow them to work with people. They like to communicate with others and prefer a flexible work environment. Influencers are more social than many people and often seek careers in sales, marketing, teaching, or customer service.

3. **Conservative Personality:** People with this personality type are usually well organized and steady in their relationships. They like harmony and value family life. Conservative personalities can sometimes be slow to accept change and are usually happiest in work that calls for special skills, such as word processing or auto repair.

4. **Recessive Personality:** People of this personality type often prefer to be in the background. They are usually detail people who enjoy work that is structured and precise. Recessive personalities might be happiest working in behind-the-scenes jobs, such as inspecting products for quality or keeping financial records.

While you may lean toward one personality type or the other, you probably have traits of all the personality types. These categories are only one means of describing personality type. If you want to find out more about your personality, ask your counselor for information on tests that you can take. One of the most frequently taken tests is the Myers-Briggs Personality Type Indicator, but other personality and interest tests are also available. Finding out your personality type doesn't tell you the specific job for you, but it can help you decide on general types of jobs, such as sales versus research.

CHAPTER 2 Getting to Know Yourself

ACTIVITY 2-6	**Workplace Competencies**
Finding Out About Careers	*Interpersonal Skills:* *Participating as a Member of a Team*

Objective: To work on a team project, negotiating responsibilities and making decisions as a team member.

Your teacher will assign you to work in a team of three to five people. After you have been assigned to a team, meet with your members and choose two different career areas to study. Since each of you will have different interests, you may have to negotiate to reach a decision about which two career areas you will study.

After making your two choices, list them in the spaces below.

Next, decide what information you want to find out about each of the two career areas. List the types of information you plan to find in the spaces under each career heading. Leave the space under "Team Member Assigned" blank for now.

Career 1: _____   **Team Member Assigned:** _____

_____   _____

_____   _____

Career 2: _____   **Team Member Assigned:** _____

_____   _____

_____   _____

When you've listed the types of information you need, decide which team member will find each type of information. After you've decided who will do what, write the name of that team member beside the assignment in the space provided.

When you have completed your research, prepare a class presentation describing the careers you chose. Use visuals to help communicate information to your classmates. In preparing for the presentation, decide how each team member will contribute to the presentation.

CHAPTER 2 Getting to Know Yourself

ACTIVITY 2-7

Finding Tomorrow's Jobs

Research

Objective: To research current information to find out which jobs are expected to offer the greatest opportunity over the next several years.

The U. S. economy changes constantly as businesses change how they operate to meet competition and to continue growing. Jobs also change with population changes. For example, when there is a jump in the birth of babies, more jobs will be available with companies that produce products and services for babies and small children. Research the jobs of tomorrow by finding the answers to the following questions using the *Occupational Outlook Handbook* at the library or online at the U. S. Bureau of Labor Statistics Web site.

1. Which ten industries are projected to grow the fastest through 2008?

_____

_____

_____

_____

_____

2. Which ten occupations are projected to grow the fastest through 2008?

_____

_____

_____

_____

3. How will education level affect job opportunities?

_____

_____

_____

4. Select four occupations that interest you. Research the projected rate of job growth and the median earnings for each occupation.

_____

CHAPTER 3   Researching Careers

ACTIVITY 3-1
Data-People-Things Preferences

Foundation Skills

*Personal Qualities:
Self-Management*

Objective: To help you determine your working preferences regarding data, people, and things.

Listed below and on the next page are 75 different jobs. Some of these jobs require working more with data, people, or things. These jobs also involve different levels of difficulty regarding data, people, and things. Read through the entire list carefully. Then choose ten jobs that you think you would most enjoy doing.

Occupation	Primarily Data, People, Things?	Code: Data, People, Things	Occupation	Primarily Data, People, Things?	Code: Data, People, Things
Accountant	D	167	Civil engineer	D	061
Actor	D	047	Clergy member	P	007
Airplane flight attendant	P	367	Clerical worker	D	362
Air traffic controller	D	162	Commercial artist	T	061
Anesthesiologist	P	101	Computer operator	T	362
Archeologist	D	067	Cook, restaurant	T	361
Architect	D	061	Copywriter	D	067
Athlete	D	341	Counselor	P	107
Bank teller	D	362	Dancer	D	047
Bellhop	P	677	Dental assistant	D	371
Biologist	D	061	Dentist	P	101
Boilermaker	T	261	Doctor	P	101
Bookkeeper	D	382	Electrician	T	381
Bricklayer	T	381	Farmer	T	161
Bus driver	T	463	Graphic artist	T	382
Butcher	T	381	Hair stylist	T	271
Buyer (retail)	D	157	Hospital administrator	P	117
Carpenter	T	381	House painter	T	381
Cashier	D	462	Interior decorator	D	051
Chemist	D	061	Iron worker	T	361
Child daycare center worker	P	677	Laborer, general	T	686
			Lawyer	P	107
Chiropractor	P	101	Librarian	D	127

(Continued on next page)

Occupation	Primarily Data, People, Things?	Code: Data, People, Things	Occupation	Primarily Data, People, Things?	Code: Data, People, Things
Machinist	T	280	Radiologist	P	101
Mail carrier	D	367	Recreation specialist	P	137
Mechanic, automobile	T	261	Salesperson, general	D	357
Model	P	667	Secretary	D	362
Motel manager	P	117	Social worker	P	107
Musician	D	041	Stonemason	T	381
Newscaster, radio or TV	D	267	Teacher	P	227
Nurse	D	374	Teacher's aide	P	327
Nurse's aide	P	674	Telephone repairer	T	281
Optician	T	280	Toolmaker	T	280
Orchard pruner	T	684	Truck driver	T	663
Personnel recruiter	P	267	University professor	P	227
Plumber	T	381	Veterinarian	P	101
Psychiatrist	P	107	Waiter/waitress	P	477
Psychologist	P	107	Welder	T	684

Write the titles of the ten jobs you prefer in the first column below. In the second column, write the letter that describes the job (D, P, or T). In the third column, write the code number that corresponds with each job.

Preferred Job	Primarily Data, People, or Things	Code: Data, People, or Things
1.		
2.		
3.		
4.		
5.		
6.		
7.		
8.		
9.		
10.		

Count the number of D's, P's, and T's listed in column 2. On the three lines below, write the total number of each, in order from largest to smallest.

Data-People-Things Preferences

First Preference _____

Second Preference _____

Third Preference _____

Now look at the code listed beside each job (column 3). The first digit of the number represents that job's difficulty regarding data, 0 being the most difficult, 1 the next most difficult, and so on. The middle digit refers to difficulty regarding people. The third refers to difficulty regarding things. Find the level of difficulty for the ten jobs you chose. Then answer the questions below.

Difficulty Level

1. Which of the jobs you preferred are easiest according to your first preference for working with data, people, or things?

   _____

   _____

   _____

   _____

   _____

2. Which of your preferred jobs are hardest according to your data-people-things preferences?

   _____

   _____

   _____

   _____

   _____

CHAPTER *3* Researching Careers

ACTIVITY 3-2	**Foundation Skills**
Career Interest Areas	*Thinking Skills: Decision Making*

Objective: To help you explore career interest areas.

As you read in your textbook, careers can be divided into clusters. The U.S. Department of Education divides careers into 16 clusters. Other sources describe careers in different ways. For example, the *Guide for Occupational Exploration* divides career interests into 12 areas:

- Artistic—creative expression of feelings or ideas
- Scientific—discovering, collecting, analyzing information about the natural world
- Plants and animals—outdoor activities (usually) involving plants and animals
- Protective—use of authority to protect people and property
- Mechanical—using machines, hand tools, or techniques
- Industrial—repetitive and specific activities in a factory setting
- Business detail—activities requiring attention to detail, primarily in office settings
- Selling—using personal persuasion and sales and promotion techniques to sell products or services
- Accommodating—providing services to others, often on a one-to-one basis
- Humanitarian—helping others with mental, spiritual, social, physical, or vocational needs
- Leading-influencing—guiding actions of others, requiring high level of verbal abilities
- Physical performing—activities performed before an audience

Within each of these interest areas are many different career possibilities. To help you pinpoint the career areas you might enjoy, decide which activity in each of the following pairs is most appealing to you. Complete all 66 questions, even though you may feel that neither choice is interesting to you. Circle the letter of your choice for each question.

1. A. Write a play.
    B. Study the causes of earthquakes.
2. C. Plant and harvest crops.
    D. Fight fires.
3. E. Direct the construction of a bridge.
    F. Teach someone to operate a machine.
4. G. Work in an office.
    H. Sell popcorn at a stadium.
5. I. Cut and style hair.
    J. Help a prison parolee find a job.
6. K. Write a computer program.
    L. Play a professional sport.

7. C. Direct a project for replanting forests.
    A. Edit a book.
8. B. Solve pollution problems.
    D. Solve a criminal case.
9. E. Design an airport.
    G. Keep business records for a company.
10. F. Work in a factory.
    H. Sell radio advertising time.
11. I. Greet hotel guests.
    K. Teach in a public school.
12. A. Paint a landscape.
    D. Investigate a burglary.

13. C. Work on a ranch.
    B. Research better ways of processing food.
14. H. Sell automobiles.
    E. Repair an automobile.
15. F. Check products for defects.
    G. Oversee clerical operations in an office.
16. I. Work as a restaurant host or hostess.
    L. Coach wrestlers.
17. J. Counsel people about careers.
    K. Work as a lawyer.
18. E. Drive a truck.
    A. Design scenery for a play.
19. B. Conduct a chemistry experiment.
    F. Operate a power sewing machine.
20. G. Use a calculator.
    C. Train racehorses.
21. D. Work as a security guard.
    H. Work in a department store.
22. J. Work at a mental health clinic.
    L. Recruit baseball players.
23. A. Photograph for a magazine.
    F. Set up machines according to written standards.
24. B. Diagnose and treat diseases.
    E. Fly an airplane.
25. C. Manage a farm.
    H. Sell furniture.
26. I. Work as a flight attendant.
    D. Join a volunteer fire department.
27. G. Compute wages for payroll records.
    J. Work in a nursing home.
28. G. Work in a bank.
    A. Act in a television series.
29. B. Take a course in astronomy.
    H. Persuade someone to buy something.
30. C. Care for an injured animal.
    I. Serve meals to customers.
31. D. Issue traffic tickets.
    J. Help patients in physical therapy.
32. E. Use hand tools.
    K. Work as a newspaper reporter.
33. F. Take an industrial arts course.
    L. Work as a circus performer.
34. H. Work as an auctioneer.
    A. Sing in a concert.
35. G. Operate a cash register.
    B. Collect rocks.
36. E. Operate heavy equipment.
    C. Grow plants.
37. F. Assemble a bicycle following drawings.
    D. Enforce fish and game laws.
38. I. Chauffeur someone.
    E. Read a blueprint.
39. J. Help the disabled.
    H. Help customers decide what to buy.
40. A. Play an instrument in an orchestra.
    I. Carry baggage.

41. B. Conduct plant/animal experiments.
    I. Work as a caddie on a golf course.
42. B. Plant and trim trees.
    J. Watch children at a daycare center.
43. D. Guard money being transported in an armored car.
    K. Research human behavior.
44. E. Repair a TV set.
    L. Play professional basketball.
45. F. Sort metal for recycling.
    J. Help a friend with personal problems.
46. L. Perform stunts for movies.
    G. Operate a telephone switchboard.
47. J. Work as an aide in a hospital.
    A. Dance in a ballet.
48. K. Work for a political campaign.
    B. Identify plants in a forest.
49. L. Work as an umpire.
    C. Pick fruit.
50. D. Guard inmates in a prison.
    E. Take a course in mechanical drawing.
51. I. Work at a health spa.
    F. Take a machine shop course.
52. K. Prepare a will.
    G. Interview people for a survey.
53. E. Manage an industrial plant.
    J. Work as a nurse in a hospital.
54. A. Write a novel.
    K. Manage health or education programs.
55. J. Take a course in psychology.
    B. Treat illnesses.
56. F. Detect differences in shape and size of materials.
    C. Fish.
57. D. Work on a rescue squad.
    G. Deliver mail.
58. K. Work as a TV news anchorperson.
    F. Assemble a toy following written instructions.
59. G. Use a computer to prepare letters.
    I. Drive a taxi.
60. H. Sell professional supplies to dentists.
    L. Compete in an athletic event.
61. L. Play soccer.
    A. Model for an artist or photographer.
62. C. Hunt.
    K. Raise funds for an organization.
63. H. Sell sporting goods.
    I. Collect tickets at a play.
64. B. Conduct an experiment to develop new metals.
    L. Referee sporting events.
65. K. Plan advertising campaigns.
    H. Sell computers.
66. L. Work as a jockey.
    D. Make an arrest.

Count the number of times you chose each letter. Write the total for each letter in the appropriate blank below.

A. _____   B. _____   C. _____   D. _____

E. _____   F. _____   G. _____   H. _____

I. _____   J. _____   K. _____   L. _____

Use the grid below to create a graph showing the number of times you chose each career area.

Career Interest Area Graph

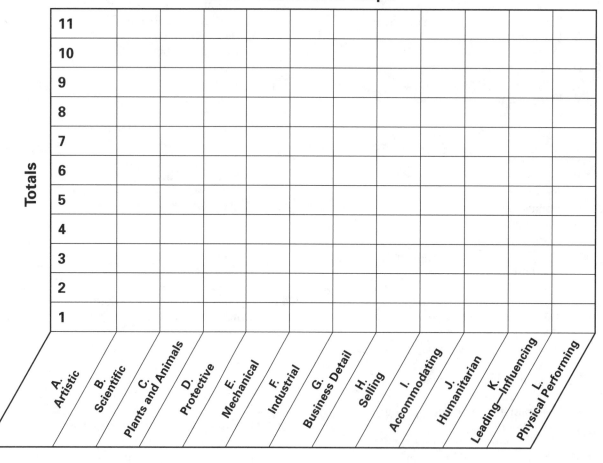

1. According to your chart, which are your three most interesting career areas?

   _____   _____   _____

2. Find more information on your career interest areas by searching the *Guide for Occupational Exploration*, the *Dictionary of Occupational Titles*, or the *Occupational Outlook Handbook*. Use these resources to find several specific occupations that you would like to learn more about. List those occupations below.

   _____   _____   _____

   _____   _____   _____

   _____   _____   _____

CHAPTER 3 Researching Careers

ACTIVITY 3-3	**Foundation Skills**
Career Consultations	*Basic Skills: Listening*

Objective: To help you learn how to conduct effective career consultations.

One good way to find out about a career in which you are interested is to talk with someone who works in that career area. A formal interview with such a person is called a career consultation. You can set up such a consultation either by telephoning or writing to the person. Whether you call or write, introduce yourself and explain the reason for your call. You may want to say that the consultation is an assignment given by one of your teachers. Set up appointments with two different people, then use the questionnaire that follows to conduct two career consultations.

Consultation 1   **Date and Time of Appointment** _____

_____   _____
Consultant's Name   Career Field

Tasks and Responsibilities
What are several of your normal job duties?

_____

_____

_____

Values
What values are important for this career?

_____

_____

Data-People-Things Relationship
Do you work mostly with data, people, or things? Please explain.

_____

_____

Work Environment
1. Do you usually work indoors or outdoors? _____

2. Do you usually work sitting at a desk, standing, or on the move? _____

(Continued on next page)

3. How much noise is there in the work area? _____

4. Is your work dangerous in any way? _____

5. If your work is dangerous, in what ways is it dangerous? _____

_____

Working Hours

1. What are your normal working hours? _____

2. How often do you work overtime? _____

3. Do you ever work nights or weekends? _____

Aptitudes and Abilities

What aptitudes and abilities are needed for your career?

_____

_____

Education and Training

What are the education and training requirements to enter and advance in your career area?

_____

_____

Salary and Benefits

1. What is the average beginning salary for someone in your career area? _____

2. How much does the average person earn after five years? _____

3. How much do the most successful people earn after ten years? _____

4. What types of benefits do workers in your career usually receive? _____

_____

Career Outlook

1. How many workers are needed in your career area at the present time?

Locally _____   Statewide _____   Nationwide _____

2. Do you think the demand for workers like you will increase or decrease in the next five years?

_____

International Opportunities

Do you work with people in other countries? How? _____

_____

Additional Comments

Is there any additional information about your career area that you think might be interesting or helpful to someone who is interested in pursuing such a career?

_____

_____

_____

Consultation 2   **Date and Time of Appointment** _____

_____   _____
Consultant's Name   Career Field

Tasks and Responsibilities

What are several of your normal job duties?

_____

_____

_____

_____

Values

What values are important for this career?

_____

Data-People-Things Relationship

Do you work mostly with data, people, or things? Please explain.

_____

_____

Work Environment

1. Do you usually work indoors or outdoors? _____

2. Do you usually work sitting at a desk, standing, or on the move? _____

3. How much noise is there in the work area? _____

4. Is your work dangerous in any way? _____

5. If your work is dangerous, in what ways is it dangerous? _____

_____

(Continued on next page)

Working Hours

1. What are your normal working hours? _____

2. How often do you work overtime? _____

3. Do you ever work nights or weekends? _____

Aptitudes and Abilities

What aptitudes and abilities are needed for your career?

_____

_____

Education and Training

What are the education and training requirements to enter and advance in your career area?

_____

_____

Salary and Benefits

1. What is the average beginning salary for someone in your career area? _____

2. How much does the average person earn after five years? _____

3. How much do the most successful people earn after ten years? _____

4. What types of benefits do workers in your career usually receive? _____

_____

Career Outlook

1. How many workers are needed in your career area at the present time?

   Locally _____ Statewide _____ Nationwide _____

2. Do you think the demand for workers like you will increase or decrease in the next five years?

_____

International Opportunities

Do you work with people in other countries? How? _____

_____

Additional Comments

Is there any additional information about your career area that you think might be interesting or helpful to someone who is interested in pursuing such a career?

_____

_____

CHAPTER 3 Researching Careers

ACTIVITY 3-4	**Foundation Skills**
Methods for Career Research	*Thinking Skills:* *Knowing How to Learn*

Objective: To help you see the various methods you can use to research careers.

Below and on the next page are descriptions of four students who have certain interests or abilities. Read the descriptions, then answer the questions about how the students should find out whether or not certain careers would be right for them. By answering these questions, you will become more skilled at doing your own career research.

1. According to an interest test he took, Jed should give serious thought to a career as a computer programmer. But Jed isn't sure exactly what a computer programmer does.

   a. What sources might Jed use to learn more about a career in computer programming?

   _____

   _____

   b. What things besides his interests should Jed think about before deciding whether or not to pursue a career in computer programming?

   _____

   _____

   c. How might Jed get the name of a working computer programmer for a career consultation?

   _____

   _____

2. Carmen has an aptitude for math. She has two decisions to make. First, she has to choose between two part-time jobs. One is a job as a waitress; the other is a clerical job in a bank. Carmen's second decision is whether to baby-sit at night to earn extra money for clothes or to take an evening computer class.

   a. How can Carmen find out more about math-related careers?

   _____

   _____

  b. Which part-time job should Carmen choose? Why?

  _____

  _____

  _____

  c. Should Carmen take the computer class or work as a baby-sitter? Why?

  _____

  _____

  _____

3. Walt wants to work in education for preschoolers.

  a. What are some things that Walt could do to get experience in this field?

  _____

  _____

  _____

  b. Judging from his career choice, what kinds of values would you say Walt has?

  _____

  _____

4. Denise is very interested in the fine arts and the humanities.

  a. How can Denise find out what jobs relate to the fine arts and the humanities?

  _____

  _____

  b. How can Denise find out about jobs currently available in the fine arts and the humanities?

  _____

  _____

  c. What kinds of part-time jobs and volunteer activities should Denise think about if she decides she would like to work in a museum?

  _____

  _____

  _____

CHAPTER **3** Researching Careers

ACTIVITY 3-5	**Workplace Competencies**
Creating a Career Search Binder	*Information:* *Organizing and Maintaining Information*

Objective: To create a personal reference binder related to career interests and research.

As you learn more about your personal skills, aptitudes, and career interests, you will collect a lot of information about careers. For example, you may want to keep the name and telephone number of a person with whom you had a career consultation in case you decide you want to ask other questions about that person's career.

For this activity, you are to create a binder of information related to your career search. You can decide what you want to place in this binder, but you might want to consider information about your interests, aptitudes and skills, career interests, and data on specific careers. Once you decide what information to include, you'll need to determine how to organize it. Use the headings and spaces below to plan the sections you'll include in your binder and the types of information to place in each section. Choose a heading for each section and then write the types of documents that will go in that section. Use extra paper if you need more space to plan your binder.

Section 1 _____

Contents: _____

_____

Section 2 _____

Contents: _____

_____

Section 3 _____

Contents: _____

_____

Section 4 _____

Contents: _____

_____

CHAPTER 3 Researching Careers

ACTIVITY 3-6

Using Library and Online Resources

Objective: To gather information on careers using the library or a career information center.

Learning as much as you can about different careers will help you make your own career choices. You can learn about careers in several different ways—through library research (using print and/or online resources), career consultations, and work. In this activity, you will first list the broad career groups in which you've identified your strongest interest. Then you'll use library references to narrow your choices. After you have chosen two careers to research, photocopy the checklist provided so that you can gather more information on each career. Useful references for beginning your career search are the *Occupational Outlook Handbook (OOH)*, illustrated below, the *Dictionary of Occupational Titles (DOT)*, and the *Guide for Occupational Exploration (GOE)*. Ask your teacher and librarian for help using these references and for suggestions of other library sources to use. For example, many public libraries have a separate section just for career information materials.

Computer Systems Analysts, Engineers, and Scientists

(O*NET 21114c, 22127, 25102, 25103A, 25104, and 25199A)

Significant Points
• As computer applications continue to expand, these occupations are projected to be the fastest growing and rank among the top 20 in the number of new jobs created over the 1998-2008 period.
• Relevant work experience and a bachelor's degree are prerequisites for many jobs; for more complex jobs, a graduate degree is preferred.

Nature of the Work
The rapid spread of computers and information technology has generated a need for highly trained workers to design and develop new hardware and software systems and to incorporate new technologies. Theses workers—computer systems analysts, engineers, and scientists—include a wide range of computer-related occupations. Job tasks and occupational titles used to describe this broad category of workers evolve rapidly, reflecting new areas of specialization or changes in technology, as well as the preferences and practices of employers.

Systems analysts solve computer problems and enable computer technology to meet individual needs of an organization. They help an organization realize the maximum benefit from its investment in equipment, personnel, and business processes. This process may include planning and developing new computer systems or devising ways to apply existing systems' resources to additional operations. Systems analysts may design new systems, including both hardware and software, or add a new software application to harness more of the computer's power. Most systems analysts work with a specific type of system that varies with the type of organization they work for—for example, business, accounting or financial systems, or scientific and engineering systems. Systems development workers are also referred to as systems developers and systems architects.

Analysts begin an assignment by discussing the systems problem with managers and users to determine its exact nature.

Your Career Interests

A. Look back at Activity 3-2 on career interest areas. List the two career areas that appealed most to you.

1. Interest Area 1 _____

2. Interest Area 2 _____

B. Refer to Activity 2-5 where you determined your general personality type. Place a check (✓) in the box next to your personality type.

☐ Dominant—Examples are managers, business owners, lawyers.
☐ Influencing—Examples are sales representatives, marketers, teachers.
☐ Conservative—Examples are word processors, auto repair persons, electricians.
☐ Recessive—Examples are accountants, quality inspectors.

Narrowing Career Choices

A. Spend some time examining the library references mentioned in your text. Try to identify specific careers that fit your personality type and career interest area preferences. List at least six of these careers in the spaces below.

_____   _____

_____   _____

_____   _____

B. Select two careers from your list that you want to research. Then use the library references mentioned in your text and the following checklist to research each of your career choices.

Career Research Checklist: Career Title _____

Resources Used _____

Tasks and Responsibilities

What are the duties and responsibilities of this career? _____

_____

_____

Values

What values are required for this career? _____

_____

Data-People-Things Relationship

1. Will this career involve working mostly with data, people, or things? _____

2. What is the difficulty rating for data, people, and things in this career? _____

Work Environment

1. Is the work done mainly indoors or outdoors? _____

2. Is the work performed while sitting, standing, or on the move? _____

3. Are indoor facilities usually air-conditioned and heated? _____

4. Is the work environment dangerous in any way? _____

Working Hours

1. What are the normal working hours? _____

2. Does the job require working weekends or nights? _____

Aptitudes and Abilities

What aptitudes and abilities are needed for this career? _____

_____

_____

Education and Training

What are the educational and training requirements needed to enter and progress in this career?

_____

_____

Salary and Benefits

1. What is the beginning salary for this career? _____

2. What is the average salary for this career? _____

3. Do workers in this career usually receive benefits? _____

International Career Outlook

Does this job involve working with people in other countries? How? _____

_____

Career Outlook

What is the long-term outlook for this career? _____

_____

_____

CHAPTER **4** Entrepreneurship

Foundation Skills

*Personal Qualities:
Speaking and Listening*

Objective: To interview an entrepreneur about his or her experiences in setting up and running a small business.

Many people choose running their own businesses as their careers. Unfortunately, almost two out of three new businesses fail within four years of opening. Lack of planning seems to be one of the most important reasons why new businesses fail. For this activity, you are to interview an established entrepreneur to learn how she or he planned for and operates the business. For your interview consider contacting business friends of your family or your supervisor if you have a part-time job. Your teacher may also suggest small-business owners you could contact.

Before you schedule an appointment for your interview, carefully read Section 4.2 in your textbook. This section will help give you ideas for your interview questions. Use the space provided below to write the questions you intend to ask during the interview. Take these questions with you when you interview the entrepreneur. In addition to writing down the answers to your questions, you may want to tape your interview, providing you receive permission to do so beforehand.

After the interview, compile your information in a report with photographs illustrating various aspects of the business. In addition to photographs, you might also use print advertisements or brochures describing the business if the interviewee has these items. Organize your report in two main sections: (1) Planning the Business and (2) Operating the Business. Later you will exchange your reports with other members of the class.

When you schedule an appointment for your interview, be sure to explain that this is a class assignment and ask permission to photograph workers performing their jobs.

Interview Questions

Planning a Small Business

_____

_____

Operating a Small Business

_____

_____

CHAPTER 4 Entrepreneurship

ACTIVITY 4-2
Preparing an Income Statement

Foundation Skills

Basic Skills: Mathematics

Objective: To complete an income statement for evaluating business profitability.

You learned in your textbook chapter that an income statement shows how much a business earns and spends during a specific period. An income statement is similar to a personal budget, which shows the amount of income for a certain time period and the various items on which that income is spent during that same time. If you are thinking about owning your own business some day, you'll need to understand the income statement and how to use it in planning for your business expenses.

For this activity, you are to use given information to calculate earnings and expenses. Using those calculations, you'll then prepare an income statement.

Here's the scenario. You and three friends started a band two years ago. You've played at school events and local events such as wedding receptions. The four of you want to make music your career now that you're out of school. Each of you owns your instrument, so you won't need to buy new instruments within the near future. You also have several sets of clothing that you use for performances. You've collected the following information about your band's business opportunities and the cost of setting up your business.

- You get two requests a month to audition for local events, mostly through word of mouth.
- Your average charge for playing at an event is $500.
- Advertising your services in the local newspaper will cost you $100 a month.
- You will need office and rehearsal space, costing $300 a month.
- Utilities for the office will cost $110 a month, including telephone expenses.
- Travel expenses to and from events are estimated at $50 a month.
- The business will need to pay salaries to each of you. The four of you decide that you can live on $300 a week each.

Choose a name for your band and write that name in the blank space at the top of the income statement form on the next page. Also fill in the month and date (use the last day of a month). Assume that your advertising pays off and you get an average of four events a month. You also get one event a month just through word of mouth. Use the average charge to calculate total earnings for a month, then record that amount on the income statement form.

Next, calculate your expenses for the month. Record each expense on the form. If you think you will have other expenses, record those expenses on the form as well.

Now find the net profit from your business.

As you can see from this activity, an income statement can be prepared as a way of planning for a business. The business owner makes assumptions about potential earnings and expenses, then calculates whether the business will earn a profit according to those assumptions.

_____

Income Statement

Month Ended _____

Revenue:

    Event fees $ _____

Operating Expenses:

    Advertising expense $ _____

    Rent for office/studio   _____

    Salaries   _____

    Travel costs   _____

    Utilities   _____

    Other expenses   _____

Total operating expenses $ _____

Net profit $ _____

Now answer these questions about your business.

1. Did you make a profit? _____

2. If you had one less event to play during the month, would you still have made a profit? _____

3. If the four of you decided that you each needed $400 a week in salaries, how many more events would you have to play to pay this added cost and still make a profit?

_____

4. If it cost you $1,500 to do an audition tape, how long would it take to pay off this expense (using the net profit you calculated above as an average monthly net profit)?

_____

CHAPTER 4 Entrepreneurship

ACTIVITY 4-3	**Foundation Skills**
Becoming an Entrepreneur	*Thinking Skills: Creative Thinking*

Objective: To help you plan how you will set up and run a small-scale business.

Your future career may be as one of the millions of small-business owners in the United States. Good planning is one of the most important factors in becoming a successful entrepreneur. Answer the following questions to help you gain a better understanding of how to plan and operate your own business.

1. What product will you sell, or what service will you provide?

_____

_____

_____

2. Where do you want to locate your business? Explain why.

_____

_____

_____

_____

3. Where will you get the money to start your business?

_____

_____

_____

_____

4. What legal form of business organization will you use? Explain why.

_____

_____

_____

_____

_____

5. How will you decide who is the customer for your product or service?

_____

_____

_____

_____

6. How will you sell your product or service to your customer?

_____

_____

_____

_____

7. How many people will you need to hire to help you run the business, and what will these employees do?

_____

_____

_____

_____

8. What kind of ratio of profit to costs will you need to avoid business failure? Explain.

_____

_____

_____

_____

9. How and where will you advertise?

_____

_____

_____

10. How will you keep records and calculate profits?

_____

_____

_____

CHAPTER  Entrepreneurship

ACTIVITY 4-4	Workplace Competencies

ACTIVITY 4-4

Communicating with Clients and Customers

Workplace Competencies

Interpersonal Skills: Serving Clients/Customers

Objective: To give you practice in choosing a message for your clients/customers and communicating that message to them.

Assume that you are a member of the musical group described in Activity 4-2. The business of your band is to provide entertainment (a service) to clients who hire you to play for an event. Communicating with potential clients, either through advertising or through one-on-one discussions, is an important means for getting future work. To help you decide on the best message for your potential clients, you first need to know who those clients are. Answer the questions that follow, then use the information to create a message promoting your services to potential clients.

1. Who is the buyer of your services: a person, a group, a business? List two different types of buyers.

_____

_____

2. Describe the characteristics of the two buyers you listed in question 1. What appeals to each of the buyers and why does each person or group buy your services?

Buyer 1   **Buyer 2**

_____   _____

_____   _____

Now choose one of the buyers you described in the preceding questions and write a message to this buyer. Your purpose is to gain the person's attention, stimulate interest in your service, and get the buyer to contact you for a possible sales presentation. Write the type of buyer to whom you are addressing your message in the blank space below, then write your message.

Buyer _____

Message _____

_____

_____

_____

_____

CHAPTER 4 Entrepreneurship

ACTIVITY 4-5
Operating a Summer Business

Objective: To learn how others have created profitable summer businesses.

When you did career research, you learned that one way to find out about a career is to get a part-time job in that career. Even if you cannot get a part-time job in your chosen career area, you can still learn about many careers by going into business for yourself. For this activity, your teacher will invite a business-person who has operated a successful summer business to your classroom.

Ask questions on the topics listed below and on the next page. Use the blank lines following each topic to write one question on that topic. Ask that question during the classroom interview and write notes about the business owner's response. After the interview, list your ideas for starting your own summer business. Compare your ideas with those of other students to "pool" your information.

Interview Questions

Selecting the Type of Business

Question _____

Response _____

_____

Location

Question _____

Response _____

_____

Financial Assistance

Question _____

Response _____

_____

(Continued on next page)

Ordering goods for sale

Question _____

Response _____

_____

Setting Prices

Question _____

Response _____

_____

Record Keeping

Question _____

Response _____

_____

Advice to Young People

Question _____

Response _____

_____

Your Ideas for a Summer Business

_____

_____

_____

_____

_____

_____

_____

_____

_____

CHAPTER 5 Developing an Individual Career Plan

ACTIVITY 5-1	**Foundation Skills**
Decision Making	*Thinking Skills: Decision Making*

Objective: To use a decision-making process in choosing a desirable place to live.

In Chapter 2 you learned about the seven-step decision-making process. These steps are:

1. Define your needs or wants.
2. Analyze your resources.
3. Identify your choices.
4. Gather information.
5. Evaluate your choices.
6. Make a decision.
7. Plan how to reach your goal.

Part of making a career decision involves deciding where you want to live. You may want to stay in your home town, move to a bigger city, or venture to another state. Use this activity to help you decide your needs and wants as they relate to where you will live. Read the information and follow the directions for each of the steps below and on the next pages.

Step 1: Define your needs or wants.

A. List ten kinds of places you would like to visit, for example, the beach or the mountains.

1. _____
2. _____
3. _____
4. _____
5. _____
6. _____
7. _____
8. _____
9. _____
10. _____

(Continued on next page)

B. Imagine and list your ten ideal homes and their location—for instance, a cabin in the mountains.

1. _____

2. _____

3. _____

4. _____

5. _____

6. _____

7. _____

8. _____

9. _____

10. _____

C. Think about the type of lifestyle you want. What parts of lifestyle are most important to you?

_____

_____

D. Name any other things you need or want in a place to live.

_____

_____

_____

Step 2: Analyze your resources.

A. Think about personal resources, such as your values. Assuming you plan to have children some day, what values do you want them to grow up with?

_____

_____

B. List five of your favorite hobbies.

1. _____

2. _____

3. _____

4. _____

5. _____

C. Name five leisure activities you want to enjoy in the future.

1. _____

2. _____

3. _____

4. _____

5. _____

D. Think about your personality and how you would feel living in the following places: the country, a large city, a small town, a suburb, an island, the woods, the desert, the mountains, the beach. Select two places that most appeal to you and explain why you think you would like living there.

_____

_____

_____

_____

Step 3: Identify your choices.

A. Location
What sections of the country do you prefer?

_____

_____

B. Climate and terrain
1. What kind of climate would you like to live in?

_____

2. What kind of landscapes do you enjoy?

_____

C. Population
What size community do you want to live in?

_____

D. Environment
1. Would you feel uneasy living near nuclear power plants or chemical or other waste sites?

_____

2. Given a choice between living in a place that has clean air and an abundant water supply or living where there is pollution but more job opportunities, which would you choose?

_____

(Continued on next page)

E. Health Care

1. How far are you willing to live from a reputable hospital?

_____

2. Is it important for you to live in a community where there is a wide selection of medical personnel from which to choose?

_____

F. Culture

Do you want to live in a place that gives you a variety of opportunities to enjoy the arts?

_____

G. Education

Is it important for you to live near a college or university?

_____

H. Recreation

What kinds of recreational facilities do you want in or near the area where you live?

_____

_____

I. Crime

Is living in an area that has a low crime rate important to you?

_____

J. Shopping

1. What kind of shopping facilities do you want near your home?

_____

2. How far are you willing to travel to shop for groceries and clothing?

_____

K. Housing

What type of neighborhood appeals to you?

_____

_____

L. Transportation

What methods of transportation should be available in your neighborhood?

_____

_____

M. Economy and Employment

1. If you liked most things about a community, would the cost of living there matter to you?

_____

2. Would you mind living in a place that has high unemployment?

_____

3. Will you use the job outlook for your career to select a place to live?

_____

Step 4: Gather information.

Consider the 13 factors listed in Step 3 as you collect information about three possible places to live. As you consider choices, think about the type of career you want and where it may be found. Good sources of information for cities and towns in the United States are:

- *America's Top-Rated Cities 2002: A Statistical Handbook.* Millerton, New York: Grey House Publishing, Inc., copyright 2001.
- *America's Top-Rated Smaller Cities 2000: A Statistical Profile*, edited by David Garoogian. Millerton, New York: Grey House Publishing, Inc., copyright 2000.
- *Moving and Relocation Sourcebook and Directory 2001: A Reference Guide to 121 Major Cities in the United States*, edited by Nancy V. Kniskern and Dawn R. Toth. Detroit, Mich,: Omnigraphics, Inc., copyright 2001.
- *Places Rated Almanac*, by David Savageau with Ralph B. D'Agostino. New York: Hungry Minds, Inc., copyright 1999.

Your school or local librarian can suggest other references. *Money* magazine conducts a yearly survey of the best places to live in the United States. Various Web sites also offer up-to-date information on housing, jobs, and living conditions in different cities across the United States.

Use separate sheets of paper to take notes on your three choices. Then answer the questions below.

A. Name the three places you chose to research.

1. _____

2. _____

3. _____

B. Name the sources you used to gather your information.

_____

_____

_____

(Continued on next page)

Step 5: Evaluate your choices.

A. Use the following checklist to rate your three choices. If the community ranks high according to your standards for a particular factor, put a plus (+) in the blank. If it ranks low, put a minus (−) in the blank. If a factor ranks neither low nor high, leave it blank.

Checklist

	Choice 1	Choice 2	Choice 3
1. Location	_____	_____	_____
2. Climate and terrain	_____	_____	_____
3. Population	_____	_____	_____
4. Environment	_____	_____	_____
5. Health care	_____	_____	_____
6. Culture	_____	_____	_____
7. Education	_____	_____	_____
8. Recreation	_____	_____	_____
9. Crime	_____	_____	_____
10. Shopping	_____	_____	_____
11. Housing	_____	_____	_____
12. Transportation	_____	_____	_____
13. Economy and employment	_____	_____	_____

B. Circle the four factors in the checklist above that are most important to you. For each choice that already has a plus for that factor, add an extra plus on the blank.

C. Write the total number of pluses (+'s) and minuses (−'s) for each of your three choices in the blanks below.

	Plus	Minus
Choice 1	_____	_____
Choice 2	_____	_____
Choice 3	_____	_____

Step 6: Make a decision.

Review everything you have written for Steps 1 through 5. Try to decide which place best matches your dreams, lifestyle goals, values, interests, personality, and greatest needs.

A. What is your best place to live? _____

B. In the space below, briefly explain your choice.

_____

_____

_____

_____

_____

_____

Step 7: Plan how to reach your goal.

List the steps you need to take to reach your goal, such as finding out which companies offer the type of career in which you are interested and are located in an area where you want to live.

_____

_____

_____

_____

_____

_____

_____

_____

_____

_____

_____

_____

CHAPTER 5 Developing an Individual Career Plan

ACTIVITY 5-2	**Foundation Skills**
Making a Flexible Career Decision	*Thinking Skills: Decision Making*

Objective: To make a flexible career decision.

You may think it's too early to choose your career, but it's important to start making some choices so you'll know what you need to do to prepare for a career. Even if you later change your mind, you will have gone through the process of evaluating different career options and making a decision. At this stage in your life, you're making a flexible career choice, which allows you to make changes later.

Review each of the personal career profiles you completed for Activity 3-6. Then fill in your answers to the questions below for each of these career choices. After evaluating both career possibilities, make your choice.

Career 1

Name of Career _____

Values
Do the values needed for this career match my personal values?_____

Duties and Responsibilities
Will I find the duties and responsibilities of this career interesting?_____

Data-People-Things Relationship
Do the data-people-things requirements in this career match up well with my own preferences?

_____

Work Environment
Will I be happy working in this environment? _____

Working Hours
Will the number of hours and the time of day worked be acceptable for my desired lifestyle?

_____

Aptitudes and Abilities
Do I have the abilities needed for this career or the aptitudes to develop them?_____

Education and Training

1. What requirements for pursuing this career have I already completed?

   _____

   _____

2. What requirements must I complete before I can enter this career?

   _____

   _____

3. What requirements must I complete in order to advance in this career?

   _____

   _____

4. Considering my grades and attendance record at school, are these educational and training requirements realistic for me?

   _____

5. Will I be able to afford the cost of this education and training? _____

Salary and Benefits

1. What is the salary range, from the entry-level salary to the salaries of the highest-paid workers?

   _____

2. Would my salary provide enough money for me to live as I want to live in five, ten, or twenty

   years? _____

3. Will all the benefits I'll need be available with this career? _____

International Career Opportunities

Will I be able to pursue interests in international opportunities in this career? _____

Career Outlook

1. What is the career outlook? _____

2. Will there be a need for many workers in this career when I am ready to begin work? _____

3. Is the long-term outlook good for this career? _____

4. Am I willing to move to another area to find a job in this career? _____

Narrowing Career Choices

1. Is this career a wise choice for me? _____

2. Why? _____

   _____

(Continued on next page)

Career 2

Name of Career _____

Values
Do the values needed for this career match my personal values?_____

Data-People-Things Relationship
Do the data-people-things requirements in this career match up well with my own preferences?

_____

Duties and Responsibilities
Will I find the duties and responsibilities of this career interesting?_____

Work Environment
Will I be happy working in this environment? _____

Working Hours
Will the number of hours and the time of day worked be acceptable for my desired lifestyle?

_____

Aptitudes and Abilities
Do I have the abilities needed for this career or the aptitudes to develop them?_____

Education and Training
1. What requirements for pursuing this career have I already completed?

   _____

   _____

2. What requirements must I complete before I can enter this career?

   _____

   _____

3. What requirements must I complete in order to advance in this career?

   _____

   _____

4. Considering my grades and attendance record at school, are these educational and training requirements realistic for me?

   _____

   _____

5. Will I be able to afford the cost of this education and training?_____

   _____

Salary and Benefits

1. What is the salary range, from the entry-level salary to the salaries of the highest-paid workers?

   _____

2. Would my salary provide enough money for me to live as I want to live in five, ten, or twenty

   years?_____

3. Will all the benefits I'll need be available with this career?_____

International Career Opportunities

Will I be able to pursue interests in international opportunities in this career? _____

Career Outlook

1. What is the career outlook? _____

2. Will there be a need for many workers in this career when I am ready to begin work?_____

3. Is the long-term outlook good for this career? _____

4. Am I willing to move to another area to find a job in this career?_____

Narrowing Career Choices

1. Is this career a wise choice for me? _____

2. Why? _____

   _____

Your Career Decision

You're now ready to make a flexible career decision. Explain in a brief paragraph what your career decision is and why you chose this career over other possibilities.

My Career Choice

_____

_____

_____

_____

_____

_____

_____

_____

CHAPTER 5 Developing an Individual Career Plan

ACTIVITY 5-3
Narrowing Your Education and Training Choices

Foundation Skills

*Personal Qualities:
Self-Management*

Objective: To set specific and realistic educational and training goals.

Before you can reach your ultimate career goal, you must set some specific and realistic planning goals for acquiring the education and training needed for your chosen career. In this activity, your school counselor will help you set some specific and realistic educational goals. In the next activity, you will use some of these planning goals when you make your plan of action. Write the answers to the following questions.

Specific Goals

1. What is your career choice?

_____

2. How much training does this career require?

_____

3. From what type of schools or training programs can you receive this training?

_____

_____

4. Select the three schools or training programs that you prefer for this training.

_____

_____

_____

5. Write your specific education and training goals.

_____

_____

_____

_____

_____

Realistic Goals

Now you will need to schedule an appointment with your school guidance counselor to see if your goal is a realistic one for you. Discuss with your counselor the information you wrote under specific goals. Ask your counselor to help you determine whether or not your goal is a realistic one for you. Answer these questions.

1. Are my grades high enough to be accepted for the training program I desire? _____

2. Is my class rank high enough? _____

3. What high school courses must I pass as a prerequisite for acceptance? _____

   _____

4. a. Will I need to take the ACT or SAT as an admission requirement? _____

   b. If so, when should I take these tests? _____

   c. How can I prepare for these tests? _____

   d. How many times should I take these tests? _____

5. What activities should I be involved in to better my chances of acceptance?

   _____

   _____

6. a. How do I apply for admission to this program? _____

   _____

   b. By what date should I apply? _____

7. a. How much financial aid will I need? _____

   b. What types of aid are available? _____

   c. How do I apply for financial aid? _____

   d. By what dates must I apply? _____

8. a. How many schools or training programs should I apply to? _____

   b. What do I do if I am rejected? _____

   c. What do I do if I am accepted by more than one? _____

9. What is probably a realistic education and training goal for me?

   _____

   _____

CHAPTER 5 Developing an Individual Career Plan

ACTIVITY 5-4	**Workplace Competencies**
Drawing Up a Plan of Action	*Information:* *Organizing and Maintaining Information*

Objective: To prepare a list of short-, medium-, and long-range career goals for use in developing a career plan of action.

For the activities in this chapter, you've answered questions about your living preferences and career interests. For this activity, you'll create a plan for actions needed to realize your dreams for a career, lifestyle, and living environment. Using spaces below, write your short-, medium-, and long-range goals. For example, a short-range goal might be to collect further information about a specific career. A medium-range goal might be to complete certain education or training. A long-range goal might be to own a home in a specific area.

Make your goals as specific and realistic as possible. Decide the date by which you want to complete each goal and the order in which you need to accomplish the goals. Revise your goals as needed as you make changes in your career plans.

Short-Range Goals   **Date for Completion**

_____   _____

_____   _____

_____   _____

Medium-Range Goals   **Date for Completion**

_____   _____

_____   _____

_____   _____

Long-Range Goals   **Date for Completion**

_____   _____

_____   _____

_____   _____

CHAPTER 5 Developing an Individual Career Plan

Research

ACTIVITY 5-5
Military Training Opportunities

Objective: To help you learn about training you can receive from the military services.

Branches of the military provide free job training in many career areas, such as electronics and computer technology. This activity will help you find out more about training you can receive through the military. Your teacher will divide the class into five groups. Each group will research topics pertaining to training provided by the Army, Navy, Air Force, Marines, or ROTC (Reserve Officers Training Corps) programs. If you are in one of the groups researching one of the four branches of the armed services, contact the nearest recruiting office of your branch to find out the following information:

1. Age, academic, and physical requirements for enlistment
2. Areas of specialized training
3. Salary at the time of enlistment
4. Opportunities for advancement
5. Benefits
6. Terms of the contract you would sign.

If you are researching ROTC, examine several college catalogs to find out the following information:

1. Age, academic, and physical requirements for enrollment
2. Type of courses
3. Pay
4. Commission for which you are eligible.

After all groups have completed their research, select one member from each group to serve on a panel to discuss military-service training. The rest of the class will record the information presented in the discussion under the appropriate headings below and on the next page.

1. **Army**

    a. Enlistment requirements _____

    b. Areas of specialized training_____

    c. Salary at enlistment _____

    d. Salary for commissioned officers_____

    e. Advancement opportunities _____

(Continued on next page)

f. Benefits _____

g. Contract terms _____

2. Navy

a. Enlistment requirements _____

b. Areas of specialized training _____

c. Salary at enlistment _____

d. Salary for commissioned officers _____

e. Advancement opportunities _____

f. Benefits _____

g. Contract terms _____

3. Air Force

a. Enlistment requirements _____

b. Areas of specialized training _____

c. Salary at enlistment _____

d. Salary for commissioned officers _____

e. Advancement opportunities _____

f. Benefits _____

g. Contract terms _____

4. Marines

a. Enlistment requirements _____

b. Areas of specialized training _____

c. Salary at enlistment _____

d. Salary for commissioned officers _____

e. Advancement opportunities _____

f. Benefits _____

g. Contract terms _____

5. ROTC

a. Enrollment requirements _____

b. Courses _____

c. Pay _____

d. Commission _____

CHAPTER 6 Finding and Applying for a Job

ACTIVITY 6-1	**Foundation Skills**
Sources of Job Leads	*Thinking Skills:*
	Creative Thinking

Objective: To begin finding sources of job leads.

Your best chance of finding out about possible job openings is to develop a list of possible contacts. Several sources of contacts are listed in the left column below and on the next page. In the blanks provided in the left column, write the names of people, agencies, newspapers, government offices, schools, or companies that might be good sources of job leads. In the blanks across from each job lead source, describe the kind of job lead that source might provide. For example, you might list "Aunt Theda" as a possible source of job leads and write "openings at the video production company where she works" as the type of job lead she might be able to give you. When you finish filling in the blanks, you should have a list of several sources you can contact for possible job leads.

Sources of Job Leads	**Type of Job Lead**

Family

_____   _____

_____   _____

Friends

_____   _____

_____   _____

Acquaintances/Neighbors

_____   _____

School Counselors

_____   _____

(Continued on next page)

Teachers

_____ _____

_____ _____

_____ _____

_____ _____

School Placement Offices

_____ _____

_____ _____

Newspaper Advertisements

_____ _____

_____ _____

_____ _____

Employment Agencies (Public and Private)

_____ _____

_____ _____

Direct Calls

_____ _____

_____ _____

_____ _____

_____ _____

Internet Contacts (include addresses)

_____ _____

_____ _____

_____ _____

_____ _____

CHAPTER **6** Finding and Applying for a Job

ACTIVITY 6-2	**Foundation Skills**
Looking at Help-Wanted Ads	*Thinking Skills:* *Knowing How to Learn*

Objective: To provide practice in finding job information in help-wanted ads.

Newspaper advertisements are an important source of job leads. From reading the job opportunities in the help-wanted section of your local newspaper, you can learn much about your local job market. If you want to find a job in another community, local bookstores usually carry newspapers from major regional and national cities. Remember, however, that only a small portion of available jobs are listed in help-wanted ads.

Below are some sample help-wanted ads, which are identified with letters A through L. Study the job information in these ads. Then in the blank spaces for the sentences that follow, write the ad letters that best complete each sentence.

A **HELP WANTED**
Sales Associate

Wanted: A friendly, outgoing person dedicated to providing exceptional customer service. We offer an excellent compensation package, performance bonus program, and health care benefits. Apply in person AM only at Clibur's Furniture, 219 E. Main Street.

B **STOP!!**
OPPORTUNITY KNOCKS

Earn $25,000 or more a year your first year. We will send you to school for two weeks expense paid, train you in the field, selling & servicing established business accounts. Must be over 21, high school grad, have car, bondable, ambitious & sports minded. Hospitalization & profit sharing. Equal Opportunity company M/F.
 Call for appointment.
880-555-3948 9 a.m.–4 p.m.

C **DECORATOR**
Paint/Wallpaper Store

Position available for experienced person for in-store decorating center. Retail sales, paint and wall covering experience necessary. We offer competitive wages and a full benefit package. Call Human Resources 555-3434. EOE.

D **HELP WANTED**
Medical/Dental

IMMEDIATE OPENING FOR EXPERIENCED DENTAL ASSISTANT. TOP WAGES & BENEFITS. SALARY ADJUSTED FOR EXPERIENCE. CALL MS. JOHNSON AT 555-3550 (AGENCY)

E **BOOKKEEPER/**
SECRETARY

Applications accepted beginning Oct. 16 for a qualified bookkeeper/secretary. Able to type and operate computer. Knowledge of accounting software preferred. References required. Excellent benefits. Apply in person. Gabriel company, 453 Water St.

F **WEB MASTER**

Local firm needs full-time, experienced Web Master to create WWW pages for computer graphic services company. FAX résumé, salary history to 612/555-0821.

G **SELL HOSPITAL**
AND MEDICAL
INSURANCE

Competitive rates, all ages, fast issue. 64 year-old company has openings for mature men and women. Mail resume to P.O. Box 1003.

H **RECEPTIONIST**

wanted evenings only. Call after 5 p.m. 555-1170.

I **HELP WANTED**
Sales Agents

SALESPERSONS WANTED for energy management products. Assertive, reliable, intelligent, professional person wanted. Good commission with draw if desired. Medical benefits. Knowledge of business community helpful. Will train. Call 555-4100.

J **COMPUTER SALES**

Experienced computer salesperson needed for local computer store for corporate sales. Potential $25–30K 1st year. Previous computer sales experience required. M–F, no wknds. Paid holidays, parking. Salary + comm. Fax resume to City Computers, 612/555-1240.

K **MANAGER TRAINEE**

Self-motivated person to operate retail shoe store. Average 40+ hrs/week. Management experience preferred. Competitive salary and benefits. Send résumé to 217 East 14th Street, Col., OH 43081.

L **SPECIAL EVENTS**
COORDINATOR

Ellison Cookware has a position for a special events coordinator to develop monthly calendar of events, such as hosting local chefs, cooking demos, and food tastings. Will also coordinate local home and bridal shows. Previous experience preferred. Apply in person, Harper's Mall. EOE

(Continued on next page)

1. The jobs that require experience are in ad(s) _____.

2. The ad(s) mentioning that experience is preferred are _____.

3. The ad(s) that mention high school or college graduates are _____.

4. Benefits are listed in ad(s) _____.

5. The ad(s) listed by employment agencies are _____.

6. The jobs that would be considered entry level are in ad(s) _____.

7. The ad(s) that require you to write or send a résumé are _____.

8. The ad(s) requiring you to call the company directly are _____.

CHAPTER  Finding and Applying for a Job

ACTIVITY 6-3

*Filling Out an
Application Form*

Objective: To give you practice in filling out a job application form.

A potential employer's first experience with you may be your application form. First impressions count in getting a job. You will do a much better job filling out your first real application form if you practice beforehand and learn the types of information required for employment applications. Complete the form on this and the next two pages as neatly as possible. Make up a job for which you are applying, or choose one of the ads in Activity 6-2.

Employment Application

Personal Data   Please Print

SOCIAL SECURITY NUMBER

Date _____

First   Middle   Last

List other first and last names you have used.

_____

Name _____

Number and Street

Address _____

_____ Apt # _____

City	County

Type of position desired

State	Zip

Date available for work

Phone No.	Area Code	Exchange	Number

Do you have any relatives employed by this company?
❏ Yes ❏ No (If yes, complete information below)

No Phone ❏

Name: _____

Date of Birth	Month	Day	Year	To be completed by those under 21 years of age.

Relationship: _____

_____

Name & Address of Employer

_____

Have you previously worked for this company or its subsidiaries?
❏ Yes ❏ No (If yes, complete information below)

Name of Company Unit: _____

Have you ever been convicted of a crime? ❏ Yes ❏ No
(Omit minor traffic citations)
(Only job related convictions are considered)

Location: _____

City & State: _____

If Yes, list all convictions showing offense and date.

Job(s): _____

Supervisor: _____

Have you ever had cash shortages or misunderstandings about funds?
(If Yes, explain) ❏ Yes ❏ No

Dates Employed: From _____ To _____

After employment, can you submit verification of your legal right to work in the U.S.? ❏ Yes ❏ No

Reason for Leaving: _____

Education

Education

(Circle total years education completed)

1 2 3 4 5 6 7 8 9 10 11 12 (High School Graduate)

13	College Freshman	16	Bachelor Degree
14	College Sophomore	17	Master Degree
15	College Junior	18	Ph D

College Information	High School Information
Undergraduate Major Field:	Name of School:
Undergraduate College/ University Attended:	Location:
Month & Year Graduated:	Major Courses Taken:
Graduate Major Field:	
Graduate College/ University Attended:	Month & Year Graduated:

Are you currently attending school? ❏ Yes ❏ No   If Yes, complete following information:

	Anticipated Graduation Date	Month	Year

Personal Data

Former Addresses within last five years

Number and Street	City	State	Zip	From Month	From Year	To Month	To Year

Military

Have you served in the United States Armed Forces?

❏ Yes ❏ No

Branch of Service _____

Highest Rank Attained _____

Indicate any skills or training acquired during military service you feel might be of interest or value in this job.

Medical

Personal Fitness Statement

Are you willing to take a physical examination at Company expense? ❏ Yes ❏ No

(Note: The work for which you have applied may involve one or more of the following job requirements: lifting, pushing or pulling 25 lbs. or more (repeatedly) and up to 60 lbs. (occasionally); lifting or extending 30 lbs. above the head (sometimes repeatedly); lifting, bending, and turning at waist simultaneously; standing or walking for at least 2 hrs. at a time; uninhibited manual dexterity; operating mechanical equipment; exposure to temperature extremes (0 to 90 degrees). If you do not know if these requirements relate to the work for which you have applied, please inquire.)

Regarding the work for which you have applied, are you substantially able to perform this work safely and without hazard to yourself and others?

❏ Yes ❏ No

In case of accident, please notify:	Name	Address	Telephone

Previous Employment

Please provide a complete report of all your working experience. List most recent employer first. Include periods of unemployment.

Company Name	From	To	Job Title	☐ Full-Time	Starting Salary $
Number and Street	Phone		Supervisor	☐ Part-Time	Final Salary
City and State	Zip Code		Reason for Leaving		$
Company Name	From	To	Job Title	☐ Full-Time	Starting Salary $
Number and Street	Phone		Supervisor	☐ Part-Time	Final Salary
City and State	Zip Code		Reason for Leaving		$
Company Name	From	To	Job Title	☐ Full-Time	Starting Salary $
Number and Street	Phone		Supervisor	☐ Part-Time	Final Salary
City and State	Zip Code		Reason for Leaving		$
Company Name	From	To	Job Title	☐ Full-Time	Starting Salary $
Number and Street	Phone		Supervisor	☐ Part-Time	Final Salary
City and State	Zip Code		Reason for Leaving		$

Have you ever been discharged or asked to resign from any position? ☐ Yes ☐ No

If your answer is yes, please explain: _____

_____

Unemployment Record	From–Mo./Yr.	To–Mo./Yr.	Brief statement covering this period if applicable
List all intervals of unemployment, if any, during the last 10 years.			

I understand that any untrue statements in this application will be just cause for dismissal.

I understand this application will be considered current for 60 days. A new application must be completed for further consideration after 60 days.

I understand that a routine inquiry may be made which will include applicable information concerning character, general reputation, personal characteristics, and mode of living. Upon written request, additional information as to the nature and scope of the report, if one is made, will be provided.

I authorize the release of information concerning my previous employment and any pertinent information they may have, personal or otherwise, and release all parties from all liability for any damage that may result from furnishing this information to Robertson's Company.

I have read and fully understand the foregoing statement.

Date_____ Signature of Applicant _____
(A copy of this statement is available upon request)

CHAPTER 6   Finding and Applying for a Job

ACTIVITY 6-4	Foundation Skills
Writing a Letter of Application	*Basic Skills: Writing*

Objective: To give you practice in writing and polishing letters of application.

Many prospective job situations will require you to send an employer a letter of application. These situations are ones in which you apply for an out-of-town job, answer a newspaper ad that asks you to apply by mail, ask for an interview from business friends of your family, or are asked by an employer to do so. In many cases, how well you write and prepare your letter of application will determine whether or not you get an interview. In this activity, you will practice writing, revising, and rewriting a letter of application.

Step 1: Writing a Draft of a Letter of Application

Look at the sample help-wanted ad below and the letter of application at the top of the next page. You may also want to refer to the sample cover letter shown in Figure 6.5 in your textbook. Get a copy of the employment section of your local newspaper and choose an ad that interests you. Be sure to choose an ad that requires a written response. Use a separate piece of paper to write the first draft of your letter of application.

> Part-time assistant needed to help customers and mix paint. Prefer high school or college student for afternoon and some evening hours. Send employment history to Richard Jefferson, Jefferson Paint & Wallpaper, 44 Bell Street, Hopedale, VA 83852.

Step 2: Revising Your Letter

Revise the first draft of your letter until it sounds right. If you are enclosing a résumé with the letter, be sure to mention the résumé. Use the checklist below to make sure the form of your letter is correct. Place a check mark (✓) beside the suggestions you have followed in your letter. Before you rewrite your letter, get a second opinion by reading it to someone else to see if it sounds clear and businesslike.

- ☐ 1. The heading includes my address and the date.
- ☐ 2. The inside address is correct.
- ☐ 3. I have used the proper salutation.
- ☐ 4. The first sentence of my letter tells where or from whom I learned about the job.
- ☐ 5. The second sentence of my letter states that I am applying for the job.
- ☐ 6. The second paragraph describes the education and experience that qualifies me for the job.

18 Apple Lane
Hopedale, VA 83851
October 17, 200X

Mr. Richard Jefferson
Jefferson Paint & Wallpaper
44 Bell Street
Hopedale, VA 83852

Dear Mr. Jefferson:

In today's News Press, your store advertised an opening for a part-time worker who would help customers and mix paint. Please consider me for this position.

Currently I am a senior at Hopedale Area High School. I have some experience working with paints and wallpaper from a building mainte-nance course. Last summer, I worked for a house-painting business. I am enclosing my résumé to assist you in reviewing my qualifications.

May I have an interview with you at your convenience? You can reach me at home at 555-7845.

Sincerely yours,

Lynn Martinez

☐ 7. The last paragraph asks for an interview and includes my telephone number.
☐ 8. I have used the correct form for my closing.
☐ 9. I have included my signature in the proper place.

Step 3: Rewriting Your Letter

After making revisions, you're ready to prepare a finished copy of your letter. Use word processing software and print your letter on good quality, white paper.

CHAPTER 6 Finding and Applying for a Job

ACTIVITY 6-5	**Workplace Competencies**
Preparing a Résumé	*Information:* *Interpreting and Communicating Information*

Objective: To help you develop skill in preparing a résumé.

Most potential employers will want to see your résumé before deciding whether or not to interview you for a job. Use the spaces below to compile the information you will need to prepare a résumé. Refer to the sample résumés in Figures 6.3 and 6.4 in your textbook. After you have collected the information for your résumé, prepare a final copy using a computer.

Name _____

Address _____

Telephone _____

Job Objective _____

Work Experience _____

_____

_____

_____

_____

_____

Education _____

_____

Honors and Activities _____

_____

Special Skills and Abilities _____

_____

References _____

_____

CHAPTER **6** Finding and Applying for a Job

ACTIVITY 6-6	**Research**

Using a Public Employment Agency

Objective: To investigate the job services offered by a public employment agency.

Public employment agencies can be a good source of job leads. Unlike private employment agencies, the services provided are free. For this activity, you are to visit your nearest public employment office. If you haven't done so already, fill out an application. You will be referred to a counselor. Answer the questions that follow by talking with the agency counselor and checking job listings.

1. What job classification and code were you assigned?

   _____

   _____

2. Have there been many listings for this job recently?

   _____

   _____

3. In general, is the rate of employment in this area good?

   _____

   _____

4. How does employment in this area compare to employment in the rest of the state?

   _____

   _____

5. How many new job openings are received daily?

   _____

   _____

6. What are the general classifications for job listings?

   _____

   _____

(Continued on next page)

7. What types of jobs seem to have several openings?

_____

_____

_____

8. What is the range in pay of jobs listed?

_____

_____

9. What process must you follow if you are interested in one of the jobs listed?

_____

_____

_____

_____

10. How often should you check the job listings in the employment office?

_____

_____

11. List the job leads you found on your visit.

_____

_____

_____

_____

_____

12. List suggestions your counselor has for you for obtaining employment.

_____

_____

_____

_____

_____

CHAPTER *7* Interviewing

ACTIVITY 7-1	**Foundation Skills**
Learning How to Interview	*Personal Qualities: Sociability*

Objective: To learn how to make the best impression possible in your job interviews.

In this activity, you are to play the role of employer. You are interviewing applicants for a job and must decide which applicant you will hire. This activity will help you see what things an employer notices about applicants during an interview. By seeing the interview from the employer's point of view, you should get a better idea of what you will need to do to be successful when you are interviewed by a real employer.

You are Alisha Carswell (the owner of Carswell's Clothing Store). You have interviewed four applicants for a sales position in the men's department. Read the descriptions of the four interviews, then write your evaluations of the applicants.

Interview 1—John Altman

John arrived about five minutes before the time scheduled for his interview. He was wearing neatly pressed slacks and an open-collar sport shirt. When you went out to the reception area to invite him into your office, you noticed that he was chatting with your secretary. You also noticed John's firm handshake when you introduced yourself and extended your hand.

John was quite a talker. He told you all about his plans to go to college and how he needed a job to finance his education. He said his grades in high school had only been average, but that was because he'd been in the band and out for several sports. John was the type of person you couldn't help but like, and the 30-minute interview seemed to fly by. He said that he hadn't had any sales experience but that he was eager to learn. John was very polite and thanked you for your time as he left. Two days later you got a thank-you note from John.

Interview 2—Kent Bennett

Kent Bennett was sitting quietly reading a magazine when you went to the reception area to invite him into your office. You commented on how sharply dressed Kent was and he laughed and said, "What do you expect? I buy all my clothes here at Carswell's." This surprised you somewhat since you ordered all the men's clothing and you didn't recognize Kent's sport coat.

Kent was all business. He sat right down and said he needed a job badly. He wanted to know how much the job paid and how much of a discount employees got on the clothes they bought at the store. Kent said he could do anything and that he had no plans for the future so you could count on his being around for a while. He said he "wouldn't be taking off to go to college or anything like all those other people do." Kent gave you lots of reasons why you should hire him. In fact you finally had to look at your watch and say you had another appointment so you could end the interview.

(Continued on next page)

Interview 3—Mark Sanchez

Mark Sanchez was wearing a dress shirt, tie, slacks, and a sport coat. When you went out to greet him, he was standing quietly reading some company notices that you had on the wall of the reception area. He smiled politely as you shook hands. As you went around behind your desk, Mark commented on what a nice office you had. You thanked him and asked him to sit down. He thanked you and sat down.

In response to your questions about education and experience, Mark said that he had received mostly A's in school and that he had worked part-time for the past two years as a cashier at a local grocery store. He said he had thought about college and that he would probably go to school someday and major in marketing. First he wanted to get some experience in sales and, since he had always been interested in clothes, he had applied for this job. As Mark talked, you noticed how carefully and precisely he worded everything.

To conclude the interview, you asked if Mark had any further questions. He asked about the starting salary. After you told him, he thanked you for your time and got up to leave. You ushered him to the door and shook hands with him. Mark smiled and said how much he'd enjoyed meeting you.

Interview 4—Kathy Powers

Kathy Powers, like John Altman, was chatting with your secretary when you introduced yourself. Kathy was nicely dressed in a tweed business suit. As she reached out to shake your hand, she smiled and said it was a pleasure to meet you.

It was obvious after only a few minutes that Kathy was very intelligent and quite articulate. She said she planned to go to college as soon as she could afford it and asked about the salary. She had worked previously at Bodikker's, your main competition, in their clothing department. She had obviously done her homework, as she seemed to know almost as much as you about your clothing department. She even made a few suggestions for updating a line of accessories.

When the interview was over, Kathy shook hands and flashed a winning smile. She seemed confident that she would get the job and said she would be seeing you.

1. If you were Alisha Carswell, which one of these four applicants would you hire? Why?

_____

_____

_____

2. If your first choice declined the job offer, which person would you then hire? Why?

_____

_____

_____

3. Which of these applicants would you *not* hire, even if you had to advertise the opening again and interview additional applicants? Why?

_____

_____

_____

CHAPTER 7 Interviewing

ACTIVITY 7-2	**Foundation Skills**
Interviewing Practice	*Personal Qualities: Sociability*

Objective: To role play interviews as a means of preparing for your own job interviews.

When getting a job can depend on a 20- to 30-minute job interview, it is only natural to be nervous about it. With good preparation and practice, however, you *can* decrease your anxiety and make a favorable impression during your interview.

At least a day beforehand, your teacher will select three or four of you to play the role of interviewee. Prepare for this interview as though it were real. Your teacher will tell you about the job opening and company. If your school has access to a video camera, your teacher will probably want to have someone tape each interview. None of the students being interviewed should be in the class at the same time as another interview is being conducted.

The rest of the class will serve as evaluators. Consider the questions under each trait listed below and on the next two pages. Then for each trait place a mark on the scale to show how you rate each applicant. Write your comments on each person's performance on page 87.

After all the interviews have been conducted, discuss your evaluations and play back portions of the interviews (if they have been taped), to emphasize important points and show where improvements could be made. Photocopy the evaluation form if you will be evaluating several interviews.

Name of Applicant _____

Appearance
Is the person well-groomed? Does he or she dress appropriately?

Poor	Fair, but needs to improve	Satisfactory	Above average	Excellent

Poise
Does the person act in a dignified manner? Do the applicant's eyes meet the interviewer's eyes often? Is the applicant's posture acceptable?

Poor	Fair, but needs to improve	Satisfactory	Above average	Excellent

(Continued on next page)

Attitude
Does the applicant seem to have a positive attitude toward people and work?

Poor	Fair, but needs to improve	Satisfactory	Above average	Excellent

Interest
How do the person's interests and career goals match the job opening?

Poor	Fair, but needs to improve	Satisfactory	Above average	Excellent

Personality
Does the applicant project a good self-concept? Will others react favorably to her or him?

Poor	Fair, but needs to improve	Satisfactory	Above average	Excellent

Use of Language
Is the person able to communicate his or her ideas effectively? Does the person use good grammar and avoid slang and jargon?

Poor	Fair, but needs to improve	Satisfactory	Above average	Excellent

Social Skills
Is the person courteous? Was the person punctual? Did the person sense when the interview was over?

Poor	Fair, but needs to improve	Satisfactory	Above average	Excellent

Preparation
Did the person being interviewed know something about the company? Did the interviewee bring a copy of her of his résumé? Were the person's answers during the interview thoughtful and well-organized?

Poor	Fair, but needs to improve	Satisfactory	Above average	Excellent

Anticipated Employment Success
How well do you expect the applicant to perform on the job?

Poor	Fair, but needs to improve	Satisfactory	Above average	Excellent

Comments

On the lines below, write any comments you may have about the interview.
Tell why you would or would not recommend the person for this job.

_____

_____

_____

_____

_____

_____

_____

_____

_____

_____

_____

_____

_____

_____

_____

_____

_____

_____

_____

_____

_____

_____

_____

_____

CHAPTER 7 Interviewing

ACTIVITY 7-3	**Foundation Skills**

ACTIVITY 7-3

*Answering Common
Interview Questions*

Foundation Skills

*Basic Skills:
Thinking*

Objective: To prepare answers to some of the most frequently asked interview
questions.

In Chapter 7 you learned that there are two basic interviewing techniques.
One method is for the interviewer to ask you to talk about yourself. The more
common method is for the interviewer to ask you specific questions. Below and
on the next page are some questions most often asked during an interview.
Decide how you would answer each question, then write your answer in the
space provided. Practicing your answers will help you to make a good impression during your job interviews.

1. What are your weaknesses? Your strengths?

_____

_____

2. What salary do you expect?

_____

_____

3. What do you want to be doing in five years? In ten years?

_____

_____

4. Why would you like to work for this company? (Pick any company.)

_____

_____

5. What questions would you like to ask?

_____

_____

6. Which courses did you like best in school? Least?

_____

_____

7. What kind of work would you like to do?

_____

_____

8. What extracurricular activities did you participate in at school?

_____

_____

_____

9. How do you spend your spare time?

_____

_____

_____

10. Do you prefer working alone or with others?

_____

_____

11. What jobs have you had? Why did you leave?

_____

_____

_____

12. How do you feel about working overtime? Evening or weekend hours?

_____

_____

13. Describe a conflict that you helped to resolve and how you did it.

_____

_____

_____

14. What skills do you think are needed to be successful in this company?

_____

_____

_____

CHAPTER 7 Interviewing

ACTIVITY 7-4
Evaluating Interview Techniques

Workplace Competencies

Interpersonal Skills: Teaching Others

Objective: To learn good interviewing techniques by coaching classmates.

Your teacher will assign you to groups of three. Meet with your group and decide on a company or job for which one of you will interview. A second person will conduct the interview. The third member of the team will observe the interview and make notes about the interview techniques of the person being interviewed. You may want to refer to the list of interviewing points in Activity 7-2. Role play the interview. Follow the guidelines below for each role.

Interviewer

1. Review the list of questions (Activity 7-3) and add others that you think are appropriate in the space below. Do not share these questions with the person being interviewed.

   _____

   _____

2. Conduct the interview in a professional manner, greeting the interviewee as if you've just met. Your role is to try to find out whether the person being interviewed has the job skills and attitude needed for the job.

Person Being Interviewed

1. Review your answers for the most frequently asked questions. Try to anticipate other questions that may be asked. Write the question(s) and your answer(s) below.

   _____

   _____

2. Prepare for the role play as you would for a real interview. Remember that actions (good manners, appearance, courtesy) are often as important in an interview as your answers to the interviewer's questions.

Observer

1. Watch the role play, making notes about both the interviewer's and interviewee's comments and behavior on a separate sheet of paper. When the role play is over, share your comments with your two team members.

2. After sharing your comments, discuss the role play as a group. Use the experience to teach each other how to improve interview performance.

CHAPTER *7* Interviewing

Research

ACTIVITY 7-5
Interview Do's and Don'ts

Objective: To research interview techniques and prepare a list of interviewing "do's" and "don'ts."

Interviewers are looking for the answers to many questions they will never ask directly in an interview. These questions relate to how the interviewer expects you to perform on the job. Such questions might be:

1. Will this person be reliable (on time, rarely absent from work)?
2. Is the applicant trainable (has basic skills and is capable of learning new ones)?
3. Will the applicant get along well with other employees?
4. Will the applicant be cooperative in doing shared work?
5. Will the applicant be healthy and able to handle the work?
6. Will the applicant present a good image for the company (dresses appropriately, is courteous, has good manners)?
7. Will the applicant be an eager worker or one who does only enough to get by?

How you answer these "unspoken" questions may determine whether or not you get the job. But how do you answer questions you aren't asked? Through your appearance, the way you speak, your manners, and your body language. Body language communicates how you feel about a situation. For example, wringing your hands or pulling at your hair indicates nervousness and uncertainty. Sitting relaxed in a chair but with good posture and continued eye contact indicates confidence.

For this activity, consult print and Internet resources on interviewing techniques. For each of the following topics, prepare a list of interviewing "do's" and "don'ts." Ask your librarian if you need help finding resources on interviewing.

DO's	DON'Ts

Appearance

_____ _____

_____ _____

_____ _____

_____ _____

_____ _____

_____ _____

(Continued on next page)

DO's	DON'Ts

Speaking Habits

_____   _____

_____   _____

_____   _____

_____   _____

_____   _____

Manners

_____   _____

_____   _____

_____   _____

_____   _____

_____   _____

Body Language

_____   _____

_____   _____

_____   _____

_____   _____

_____   _____

CHAPTER 8 Beginning a New Job

ACTIVITY 8-1	**Foundation Skills**
On-the-Job Case Studies	*Personal Qualities: Responsibility*

Objective: To help you become more aware of problems or difficult situations you may encounter at work.

Both employers and employees can expect certain behavior of each other. Problems arise when expectations are not met. Read the following case studies and answer the questions to learn more about dealing with employer-employee problems.

Case 1 A number of customer complaints have been made to the manager of a small department store about the poor service of the salesclerks. Most of the complaints mentioned situations taking place between noon and 1 p.m. Because customer traffic is quite heavy during this time, the manager has requested that all employees be on the floor during that hour each day. Lunch hours now are to be taken only between 11 a.m. and noon or between 1 and 2 p.m.

Barbara has been taking her lunch hour at noon since she began working in the store three years ago. As she usually has lunch with a friend, Barbara has continued leaving at noon. The manager noticed this and warned her that if it occurred again she would be fired. Barbara, thinking that after three years she had earned the right to a noon lunch hour, felt the manager was being unfair.

1. Does Barbara have a right to continue taking a noon lunch hour? Why or why not?

_____

_____

2. How could this disagreement have been avoided?

_____

_____

Case 2 Kurt, 19, was an accounting clerk for a local service station. He was new to this job, and Mr. Jones, his employer, decided to test his honesty. He placed five dollars extra in the cash register to see what Kurt would do about it. Kurt decided to keep the five dollars for himself because the money in the register was "over." He knew that he should record it in the "cash short and over" ledger, but he didn't. His employer fired him. Mr. Jones told Kurt that if he would take a small amount now, he might take a larger amount later.

(Continued on next page)

1. Do you think Kurt was dishonest? Explain why.

_____

_____

2. Do you think Kurt's employer should have fired him? Why or why not?

_____

_____

Case 3 Dave and Laura are administrative assistants in a large corporation that manufactures electrical parts. Laura always arrives at work 10 or 15 minutes late. Then she goes to the ladies' room to put on her make-up. She finally gets to her desk about 8:30 A.M. Dave always arrives at his desk promptly at 8 A.M. and begins work. Even though Laura has better computer skills than Dave, Dave got a raise when it came time for a salary review, but Laura didn't.

1. Do you think Laura's employer had a right to hold back her raise for being late? Why or why not?

_____

_____

2. If you were Laura, what would you do to improve your chances of getting a raise next time?

_____

_____

Case 4 Eric, age 17, was a waiter at a restaurant during the summer after his junior year in high school. During the lunch period, all the waiters were very busy. After the lunch rush, however, most of the waiters sat down to drink a soda, eat, or just relax. Eric never sat down on duty. He kept busy cutting up lemons for tea or filling napkin holders and salt and pepper shakers. He could always see what needed to be done, and he did it. The restaurant manager noticed Eric's initiative and gave him a dollar-per-hour raise.

1. If you were Eric's boss, would you have given him the raise? Why or why not?

_____

_____

2. Do you believe that time seems to pass faster when you are busy? Why or why not?

_____

_____

3. People who show initiative are not always given pay raises right away. Suppose you felt that you wouldn't be getting a raise soon. Would it still be worth the effort to look around to see what needed to be done and do it? Why or why not?

_____

_____

Case 5 Walter, 20, worked in Graham's Garage. He was unusually slow in performing brake jobs for customers. Since customers were charged for the hours of labor, they ended up paying more for Walter's jobs. When the supervisor tried to show Walter how to do the work faster, he refused to listen. He said that his way was best. Walter had shown a similar attitude about other jobs around the garage. Because of his unwillingness to learn, Walter's supervisor finally had to fire him.

1. Could Walter's supervisor have done anything to make him a more productive worker?

_____

_____

2. If you were an employer, what would you do about an employee who was unwilling to learn?

_____

_____

Case 6 Ted, 18, is a data-entry clerk for a local accounting firm. His employer gives him directions on how to set up the charts for each job. Sometimes Ted changes the format slightly, thinking his way is better, only to have the work returned to be redone. After Ted was late with a report because it had to be redone, Ted's employer warned him that if he failed to follow directions again, he would be fired.

Suppose that Ted's way is the better way. Should he still do it his employer's way? Why or why not?

_____

_____

Case 7 The Home Improvement Center hired Arnold part-time to stack lumber, make deliveries, and assist wherever needed. His duties for a particular day were not usually known ahead of time. Each afternoon he was given directions when he reported for work. Last Tuesday he was stacking lumber. When he finished the job early in the afternoon, his boss told him to take the rest of the day off since everything seemed to be caught up. The next day Arnold didn't show up for work at all. When he came in on Thursday afternoon, the boss told Arnold he was fired. On Wednesday morning the center had made many sales that were to be delivered that afternoon. Since Arnold didn't show up or call in, the manager had to hire another person to make the deliveries.

(Continued on next page)

1. Was the manager unfair to Arnold? Explain.

_____

_____

2. Suppose that Arnold had been ill on Wednesday. What could he have done to save his job?

_____

_____

Case 8   Elena, 18, recently completed high school and now has a job as a receptionist in a savings and loan company. She gets bored with her job and rarely smiles at people who come into the bank. Instead she chats with her coworkers. She dislikes going to work every morning.

What could Elena do to increase her enthusiasm?

_____

_____

Case 9   Janet was a checker in a large grocery store. She was a good worker, very dependable, and never late for work. However, she made at least one mistake a day on her cash-register receipts because she didn't carefully count the change she returned to customers. To explain her errors, Janet left notes with her cash register receipts. The manager soon became tired of this. She suggested that Janet slow down a little and try to be more accurate. Janet became very upset and quit because she could not accept constructive criticism.

What would you have done in Janet's place?

_____

_____

Case 10   "I don't like working for Ms. Jones," said Joan to her friend, Lynn, one day at lunch. "I'd rather work for Mr. Baxter. At least he takes interesting cases."

A lady at the next table overheard Joan and Lynn's conversation. Since she was a friend of Ms. Jones, she repeated to her what she had heard. The office atmosphere suddenly became very strained.

1. Who was the cause of the unpleasant office atmosphere? Why?

_____

_____

2. If you find that you simply have to complain about your job to everyone you know, what should you do?

_____

_____

Case 11 Martha's career goal is to be a police officer. She was thrilled when she was admitted to the police academy. She graduated near the middle of her class. At her first job evaluation, Martha was told that she was behind in her paperwork and that she needed to improve her driving skills. Martha loves her work and is determined to do well at it.

1. If you were Martha, how would you react to this evaluation? Why?

_____

_____

2. What should Martha do to get a better evaluation next time?

_____

_____

Case 12 Lionel is a carpenter's apprentice. His latest job is rough-forming walls for the new addition to the courthouse. The supervisor on the job told Lionel to use the table saw to cut the studs for the wall to length. Then the supervisor left to talk with some other workers. Lionel has watched other carpenters use the table saw, but he has never used one himself.

If you were Lionel what would you do? Why?

_____

_____

_____

_____

CHAPTER 8 Beginning a New Job

ACTIVITY 8-2	**Foundation Skills**
The Effect of Appearance	*Personal Qualities: Sociability*

Objective: To learn how appearance affects other people's impressions of you.

For this activity, use magazines to find illustrations of four men and four women. Each person should have different grooming and clothing. After you have found your eight illustrations, tape or glue them onto pages 100 and 101. Then show these illustrations to three adults and ask them the following questions:

1. What total yearly salary would you guess each person earns?
2. What kind of work do you think each person does?
3. Which man and which woman would you ask for help in getting a good job?
4. If these eight people all offered you similar investment opportunities, who would you invest your $50,000 with?

Do not tell the adults you interview that you are surveying the effect of dress and grooming. Write their answers in the blanks provided below and on the next page. Then hold a class discussion about how appearance affected the answers of the adults you interviewed.

Adult 1

1. What might be a yearly salary for the person in illustration

A? _____ D? _____ G? _____

B? _____ E? _____ H? _____

C? _____ F? _____

2. What kind of work might be done by the person in illustration

A? _____ D? _____ G? _____

B? _____ E? _____ H? _____

C? _____ F? _____

3. Which man and woman would you ask for help in getting a good job?

Man _____ Woman _____

4. Which person would most likely be your choice to invest your money? _____

Adult 2

1. What might be a yearly salary for the person in illustration

   A?_____   D?_____   G?_____

   B?_____   E?_____   H?_____

   C?_____   F?_____

2. What kind of work might be done by the person in illustration

   A?_____   D?_____   G?_____

   B?_____   E?_____   H?_____

   C?_____   F?_____

3. Which man and woman would you ask for help in getting a good job?

   Man _____   Woman _____

4. Which person would most likely be your choice to invest your money?_____

Adult 3

1. What might be a yearly salary for the person in illustration

   A?_____   D?_____   G?_____

   B?_____   E?_____   H?_____

   C?_____   F?_____

2. What kind of work might be done by the person in illustration

   A?_____   D?_____   G?_____

   B?_____   E?_____   H?_____

   C?_____   F?_____

3. Which man and woman would you ask for help in getting a good job?

   Man _____   Woman _____

4. Which person would most likely be your choice to invest your money?_____

(Continued on next page)

A

B

C

D

E   F

G   H

CHAPTER 8 Beginning a New Job

ACTIVITY 8-3	**Foundation Skills**
The Importance of Appearance	*Personal Qualities: Self-Management*

Objective: To learn how appearance can help you achieve your career goals.

You know from Chapter 7 that it is important to present a good appearance during your job interview. Appearance is also important when you begin your new job. The following cases show how employees can benefit from or be hurt by the way they look on the job. Read each case carefully and then answer the questions that follow it.

Case 1 Dwight and Roger have been hired as telemarketers to sell consumer products over the phone. A number of people who have held this job in the past have been promoted to sales positions that involve calling on customers in person. Dwight wears a jacket and tie to work every day. Roger feels that since the people he calls can't see him, he might as well wear jeans and be comfortable. After several months, Roger has a slightly better sales record than Dwight. The company needs a new sales representative.

1. If you were the employer, would you promote Dwight or Roger? Why?

_____

_____

2. Roger feels that it is only the customer he needs to impress. Do you agree? Why or why not?

_____

_____

Case 2 Lin is a telephone receptionist in the headquarters of a major corporation. She would like to be an administrative assistant there. Looking around, Lin notices that most of the receptionists wear jeans and T-shirts to work. The administrative assistants all dress neatly in skirts or dresses, or suits and sports jackets. Very few receptionists have ever been promoted in the company. Lin decides to dress as though she is already an administrative assistant.

1. Do you think Lin has a better chance of being promoted than the other receptionists? Why or why not?

_____

_____

2. Who is Lin really dressing for? Do you agree or disagree with her plan?

_____

_____

Case 3 Leon stocks shelves at the neighborhood grocery store. Shortly after he was hired, he got a part in the school play. The part called for Leon to have long hair and a scraggly beard, so Leon stopped shaving and cutting his hair. Because he was always in a hurry, he appeared for work in whatever clothes he happened to be wearing—usually old pants, sneakers, and a sweatshirt. Although Mr. Allen, Leon's boss, couldn't say specifically why, he found himself becoming irritated every time he saw Leon. Leon continued to do a good job, but Mr. Allen just muttered and shook his head every time he saw him. Then the play was over. Leon shaved, cut his hair, and came to work in a clean shirt and tie. At the end of the day, Mr. Allen patted Leon on the back and said, "Good work! I was afraid you weren't going to make it for a while. However, if you keep working the way you did today, you'll do all right." Actually, Leon's work hadn't changed at all.

1. How do you think Leon should have replied to Mr. Allen's statement?

_____

_____

2. Assuming he wants to do well at his job, how should Leon appear for work in the future?

_____

_____

Case 4 Ken and Lewanda were hired to give tennis lessons during the summer at a local tennis club. Anyone interested in the lessons was entitled to a free demonstration from one of the teachers. Ken wore cut-off jeans and no shirt for his demonstrations. Lewanda wore proper tennis clothes and tied her hair back neatly. Both were good players and teachers.

If you ran the tennis club, which instructor would you invite to return next summer?

_____

_____

_____

CHAPTER 8 Beginning a New Job

| ACTIVITY 8-4 | **Workplace Competencies** |
| *Making Time Decisions* | *Resources:*
Allocating Time |

Objective: To learn to schedule work activities.

You have just started a new job at the WJYX radio station. Your job duties are to open and catalog the music CDs sent to the station, to file the CDs in the appropriate place, and to create a computer record of the artist, song title, and the file location. You'll also help the deejays research songs for special radio programs.

On your first day of work, you report to the Human Resources Department at 8:30 A.M., the normal starting time. After filling out the necessary paperwork, you report to your boss. Now it's 9:30 A.M. and your boss has just finished giving you a list of activities that need to be done today. These activities are listed below, along with the approximate amount of time each will require. The activities are not listed in order; you will need to decide what to do first.

Use the list to schedule the remainder of your work day. You have an hour for lunch that must be taken between 11:30 A.M. and 1:30 P.M. and a 15-minute break in the afternoon. The normal quitting time is 4:30 P.M. Use the time outline on the next page to complete your schedule.

Work Assignments

1. View orientation and benefits videotape (30 minutes).

2. Open the packages of CDs that arrived yesterday (16 packages) and make a list of the contents. Opening a package and making a list of the artist and the song title will require about 15 minutes per package.

3. You will attend a meeting at 2:00 P.M. to discuss an upcoming program one of the evening deejays is planning. The meeting will take an hour.

4. Three of the packages contain new CDs the evening deejay wants to use for the special program. You'll need the list of artists and song titles from these packages for the 2 o'clock meeting. You'll need about 30 minutes to input the list into the computer and prepare a printout for the meeting.

5. Your boss wants you to write a memo notifying all the deejays of a meeting a week from today. The memo will take you about 20 minutes to write, print out the copies needed, and put them in the interoffice mail.

Daily Schedule

8:00 a.m. _____

8:30 a.m. _____

9:00 a.m. _____

9:30 a.m. _____

10:00 a.m. _____

10:30 a.m. _____

11:00 a.m. _____

11:30 a.m. _____

12:00 noon _____

12:30 p.m. _____

1:00 p.m. _____

1:30 p.m. _____

2:00 p.m. _____

2:30 p.m. _____

3:00 p.m. _____

3:30 p.m. _____

4:00 p.m. _____

4:30 p.m. _____

5:00 p.m. _____

1. If you could not complete all the assignments by 4:30, what would you do?

_____

_____

_____

2. How does planning your work help you solve problems?

_____

_____

_____

CHAPTER *8* Beginning a New Job

ACTIVITY 8-5	**Research**
Exploring Employee Benefits	

Objective: To learn about credit unions as an employee benefit.

One of the benefits that many companies offer their employees is the opportunity to join a credit union. A credit union is a financial institution that is set up for the members of a certain group, such as the employees of a company. Only members of the credit union can use its services. Credit unions can be a good place to start a savings account or to borrow money for a major purchase.

Find a local business that has a credit union. Call the director of the credit union and get answers to the questions below. Be sure to explain that you are doing this as part of a school project.

1. What are the benefits to employees of a credit union?

   _____

   _____

   _____

2. What is required for a person to join the credit union at this company?

   _____

   _____

3. When you have savings in a commercial bank, they are protected by the government through the Federal Deposit Insurance Corporation. Are credit union savings protected? How?

   _____

   _____

4. What types of loans can a commercial bank make that a credit union cannot?

   _____

   _____

5. What would this credit union charge a member for a new car loan? Compare this amount with the charges at a local bank. Which offers the better deal?

   _____

   _____

   _____

CHAPTER 9 Workplace Ethics

ACTIVITY 9-1	**Foundation Skills**

ACTIVITY 9-1

Developing Listening Skills

Foundation Skills

*Basic Skills:
Listening*

Objective: To learn how to listen carefully and take notes to enhance memory.

You may think that listening requires no particular skill. It's just something you do naturally. In a work setting, however, being able to listen effectively can make a difference between job success and job failure. How do you listen effectively? You clear your mind of distractions and focus on the speaker and what is being said. Taking quick notes can also help you. Be careful, though, that taking notes does not distract you so much that you fail to hear what is being said after you start writing a note.

For this activity, your teacher will read some directions. Use the space below to take notes to help you remember the directions. You will *not* be allowed to ask questions when your teacher has finished reading the directions.

Notes:

_____

_____

_____

_____

_____

_____

_____

_____

_____

_____

_____

_____

(Continued on next page)

Now use your notes and your memory of what you heard to create the object described. Then answer these questions.

1. Were you able to follow the directions successfully to create the item described?

_____

2. If you were able to complete the activity, what helped you most: listening carefully, taking notes, recognizing the item to be created?

_____

_____

_____

_____

3. How can you relate this activity to on-the-job performance?

_____

_____

_____

_____

4. If you were not able to complete the activity successfully, what would have helped you to be successful?

_____

_____

_____

_____

5. If you were to repeat an activity of this type, what would you do differently to help you be successful?

_____

_____

_____

_____

CHAPTER 9 Workplace Ethics

ACTIVITY 9-2	**Foundation Skills**
Developing Workplace Skills	*Thinking Skills: Reasoning*

Objective: To demonstrate how cooperativeness, initiative, responsibility, and self-management can help you be more successful.

Employers value workers who demonstrate the skills of cooperativeness, initiative, responsibility, and self-management. Developing these skills will help you to be a more productive employee. As a productive worker, your potential rewards are higher raises and promotions to better jobs.

To learn more about workplace skills, read each of the following cases. Then answer the questions relating to each case.

Case 1 Dana, Caryl, and Janson have been assigned to complete an inventory of the products in stock in a convenience store where they work. The supervisor has left it up to the three of them to decide how to split the work. They have a deadline of three days to complete the report.

Dana wants to enter the information in the computer for preparing the report but does not want to count items on the shelves because that is boring. Caryl wants only to work in the open-shelf sections because the freezer items are too cold. Janson prefers to organize the work and make assignments for the other two to follow. The three have spent at least two hours arguing about how to complete the inventory. They have yet to count the first shelf of products.

1. What workplace skills are Dana, Caryl, and Janson ignoring?

_____

2. Why are Dana, Caryl, and Janson behaving in this way?

_____

_____

3. What will be the likely result of this work assignment?

_____

_____

4. If you were a member of this team, what would you do?

_____

_____

(Continued on next page)

Case 2 You work as a sales clerk in a large department store. You usually
arrive at work a few minutes early. Today when you got to your station, ten minutes before you are officially to begin work, you found
the two sales clerks on duty standing at the cash register talking to
each other and preparing to close their registers. A customer was
standing near the register looking annoyed and frustrated.

1. What would you do in this situation?

_____

_____

_____

2. What workplace skills are the two sales clerks who are on duty demonstrating that they lack?

_____

_____

3. How might the behavior of the two sales clerks affect the department store's business?

_____

_____

_____

4. If you were the department supervisor, what would you say to the two sales clerks who were
   ignoring a customer?

_____

_____

_____

5. As the clerk observing poor work habits of coworkers, what would you do? Would you report
   your coworkers' behavior to the supervisor? Why or why not?

_____

_____

_____

_____

Case 3 Kenisha and Selena work as sales associates in a local building supply and consumer products superstore. Kenisha works in the paint and home decoration department. During times when she is not busy with customers, Kenisha checks the shelves to make sure they are fully stocked. If a certain item is out of stock, she checks the inventory in the computer. If the item is in the warehouse, she'll call and find out when it will be restocked on the shelves so she can provide that information to customers.

Selena works in the garden supplies department. She knows very little about plants and doesn't care to learn about them. This job will be good enough until she can find something better. When customers ask Selena questions she can't answer, she sends them to another sales associate for help. Selena frequently complains to family and friends that she isn't being paid enough to spend her time learning new job skills.

1. What workplace skills are being demonstrated by Kenisha and Selena?

_____

_____

_____

2. As a supervisor, how would you evaluate Kenisha?

_____

_____

_____

3. How would you evaluate Selena?

_____

_____

_____

4. As a friend, what would you tell Selena about her attitude?

_____

_____

_____

CHAPTER 9 Workplace Ethics

ACTIVITY 9-3	**Foundation Skills**
The Role of Ethics	*Personal Qualities: Integrity/Honesty*

Objective: To learn how to apply ethical behavior to workplace issues.

As you read in your textbook chapter, as many as one-third of all employees interviewed in a survey observed some type of unethical behavior by coworkers. Some people may knowingly follow unethical practices. Others may just not realize that their behavior is unethical.

For this activity, read each of the cases and then answer the questions that follow.

Case 1 You work on an assembly line for a large corporation that manufactures in-line skates and other sporting goods. This company follows a team approach to manufacturing and allows its employee teams to make decisions about how the work will be done.

One of the members of your team has been complaining that the conveyor line moves too fast. The other team members disagree. You observe the complaining coworker deliberately shove a half-finished skate into the machine controlling the conveyor belt to cause it to malfunction. When this week's team leader came over to ask what was the problem, the employee said that one minute the conveyor belt was fine, the next it just stopped. Should you tell the team leader what you saw?

1. Is this action against the law? _____

2. Do you know the action is wrong? _____

3. Is the action contrary to company values? _____

4. Will you feel bad if you perform this action? _____

5. If this action were reported on the five o'clock news, what would viewers think about it?

_____

_____

_____

Case 2 You work for a large automotive repair company as a mechanic's assistant. The company performs a lot of oil changes for customers and thus has to dispose of the used oil. Local ordinances require that oil be disposed only in certain places because pouring it into sewer drains can contaminate local water supplies. Most of the company's employees follow its policy of placing used oil in the proper containers for hauling to a disposal site. One mechanic with whom you work frequently tells you to dump the oil down the drain to save time.

1. Is this action against the law? _____

2. Do you know the action is wrong? _____

3. Is the action contrary to company values? _____

4. Will you feel bad if you perform this action? _____

5. If this action were reported on the five o'clock news, what would viewers think about it?

_____

_____

Case 3 You work as a telephone sales representative for a computer software company. When you started your job, you were required to sign a document about keeping company information confidential. Sitting in the company cafeteria one day, you overhear some of the programmers discussing a software bug in a new program that they have been unable to fix. The new program is supposed to ship to customers within one week. If the programmers hold the software to fix the bug, its release will be late. If the programmers release the software and try to fix the bug later, the company may have a lot of irate customers.

At dinner with a friend who works for a competing computer software company, you find yourself about to mention the bug in the new software.

1. Is this action against the law? _____

2. Do you know the action is wrong? _____

3. Is the action contrary to company values? _____

4. Will you feel bad if you perform this action? _____

5. If this action were reported on the five o'clock news, what would viewers think about it?

_____

_____

CHAPTER 9 Workplace Ethics

ACTIVITY 9-4	**Workplace Competencies**
Understanding Cultural Differences	*Interpersonal Skills: Working with Cultural Diversity*

Objective: To learn about coworkers' values and how they affect you.

Residents of the United States belong to many different ethnic groups. Each group may have its own traditions and different ways of interacting with people. In the business world, you will encounter people with many opinions and expectations that are different from yours. Accepting and working with these differences will help you be more successful in your own work.

Read the following case, then answer the questions. You may want to read an article or refer to some books on working with different cultures to help you answer the questions.

> Beth works for a company that has offices in several different countries. Employees from foreign offices often spend a few weeks or even months in the U.S. office completing training programs and working in various departments. In her job as an assistant to the vice president for training and development, Beth works with most of these employees. Beth schedules training sessions and follows up with employees to make sure they have completed the training activities assigned.
>
> Beth sometimes has difficulty getting some employees to attend the sessions she schedules for them. For example, an employee from Israel did not show up for a session scheduled for a day on which a religious holiday began. Other employees, mostly those from Latin American countries and parts of Europe, are often late for sessions scheduled immediately after lunch.

1. Why might Beth be having difficulties with some of the trainees?

_____

_____

_____

_____

_____

_____

2. What specific cultural differences might account for Beth's difficulties?

_____

_____

_____

_____

3. What could Beth do to learn why she is having problems with some of the trainees?

_____

_____

_____

_____

4. How might Beth overcome these difficulties?

_____

_____

_____

_____

5. What would you do in Beth's place?

_____

_____

_____

_____

CHAPTER *9* Workplace Ethics

ACTIVITY 9-5

*Finding Out About
Company Policies*

Objective: To learn how companies deal with ethical issues.

   Some companies have formal policies describing the ethical behavior
employees are expected to maintain. An example of an ethics policy might be a
rule that employees who make buying decisions cannot accept gifts from the
vendors from whom they buy.

   For this activity, you are to research the ethics policies of several local businesses. Choose a local business, then call the director of human resources.
Explain that you are completing a school project and ask whether the company
has a formal ethics policy. If the company has no written policy, ask the director
to share information about how the company deals with ethical issues.

   Your teacher will assign you to teams of four to five members to complete
this activity. As a team, decide which actions you need to take, which businesses you will call, and the responsibilities of each team member. When you are
ready to conduct the research, record information on the questionnaire below or
create your own questionnaire. Make a copy of this page for each company you
plan to call.

Name of company _____

Name of director of human resources/telephone number _____

1. Does your company have a written policy on the ethical behavior expected of your employees?

   _____

2. What types of situations are covered by ethics policies?

   _____

   _____

   _____

3. What actions are taken when employees violate ethics policies (for example, giving employees
   written warnings, putting employees on probation, dismissal)?

   _____

   _____

   _____

CHAPTER 10 Developing a Positive Attitude

ACTIVITY 10-1
An Attitude Inventory

Foundation Skills

Personal Qualities:
Sociability

Objective: To help you evaluate your attitude toward other people and situations to see if you need to improve your attitude.

One of the primary reasons why young workers lose their jobs is because they don't get along well with others. In other words, they have a negative attitude. To see if your own attitude needs improvement, complete the attitude inventory that follows.

In the blank to the left of each statement below, write the number of what you believe is the most accurate answer according to the following scale.

5 = positively yes
4 = mostly yes
3 = undecided
2 = mostly no
1 = positively no

After you have answered all the questions, total your score. Then rate your attitude according to the scale at the end of the activity.

_____ 1. Do you make new friends easily?

_____ 2. Do you try hard not to be a complainer?

_____ 3. Are you careful never to interrupt when another person is speaking?

_____ 4. Can you be optimistic when others around you are depressed?

_____ 5. Do you try not to boast or brag?

_____ 6. Do you control your temper?

_____ 7. Are you genuinely interested in the other person's point of view?

_____ 8. Do you speak well of your employer?

_____ 9. Do you keep the same friends for years?

_____ 10. Do you feel well most of the time?

_____ 11. Do you refrain from swearing?

_____ 12. Do you keep promises?

_____ 13. Are you at ease with the opposite sex?

_____ 14. Do you try to be helpful to others?

_____ 15. Do you organize your work and keep up with it?

(Continued on next page)

_____ **16.** Do you get along well with your parents?

_____ **17.** Do you readily admit your mistakes?

_____ **18.** Can you be a leader without being bossy?

_____ **19.** Is it easy for you to like nearly everyone?

_____ **20.** Can you stick to a tiresome task without being constantly urged along?

_____ **21.** Do you realize your weaknesses and attempt to correct them?

_____ **22.** Can you take being teased?

_____ **23.** Do you avoid feeling sorry for yourself?

_____ **24.** Are you courteous to your fellow workers?

_____ **25.** Are you usually well-groomed and neatly dressed?

_____ **26.** Are you a good loser?

_____ **27.** Do you enjoy a joke even when it is on you?

_____ **28.** Do you like children?

_____ **29.** Do you keep your own room in good order?

_____ **30.** Are you aware of the rules of etiquette?

_____ **31.** Are you tolerant of other people's beliefs?

_____ **32.** Do you respect the opinions of your parents?

_____ **33.** Do you know how to make introductions easily and correctly?

_____ **34.** Do you avoid sulking when things do not go as you would like?

_____ **35.** Are you a good listener?

_____ **36.** Do you like to attend parties?

_____ **37.** Are you the kind of friend you expect others to be?

_____ **38.** Do you accept compliments or gifts graciously?

_____ **39.** Can you disagree without being disagreeable?

_____ **40.** Do you like to give parties?

_____ **41.** Can you speak before a group without feeling self-conscious?

_____ **42.** Are you usually on time for social engagements?

_____ **43.** Do you drive carefully?

_____ **44.** Do you generally speak well of other people?

_____ **45.** Do you smile easily?

_____ **46.** Can you take criticism without being resentful or feeling hurt?

_____ **47.** Are you careful to pay back all loans, however small?

_____ **48.** Does your voice usually sound cheerful?

_____ **49.** Can you work well with those you dislike?

_____ **50.** Do you contribute to the conversation at the family dinner table?

_____ **51.** Do you try as hard to get along well with your family as with friends?

_____ **52.** Do you like people who are much older than you?

_____ **53.** Are you pleasant to others even when you feel displeased about something?

_____ **54.** Do you show enthusiasm for the interests of others?

_____ **55.** Are you free from prejudices?

Rating Your Attitude

250–275   You're too good to be true!

200–249   Your attitude toward others is very good.

150–199   Your attitude needs improvement.

Below 150 You need to make a careful study of your attitude toward others, looking at yourself as others see you! Then you need to begin working toward improving your attitude.

What was your score? _____

What steps will you take, if needed, to improve your attitude?

_____

_____

_____

_____

_____

_____

_____

_____

_____

_____

_____

_____

_____

_____

CHAPTER *10* Developing a Positive Attitude

ACTIVITY 10-2
Rating Your Personal Traits

Foundation Skills

Personal Qualities:
Self-Management

Objective: To help you consider which of your personal traits may need improvement.

One of the ways you can increase your effectiveness in relating to others is to improve your personal traits. First, though, you need to become aware of the strengths and weaknesses in your personality.

Listed below are 19 personal traits. Place a check mark in the column that best describes you with regard to each trait. Be honest with yourself.

Personality Rating

Trait	Excellent	Good	Fair	Poor	Very Poor
Attitude					
Common sense					
Courtesy					
Dependability					
Enthusiasm					
Foresight					
Friendliness					
Health					
Honesty					
Initiative					
Loyalty					
Motivation					
Neatness					
Open-mindedness					
Punctuality					
Self-control					
Sense of humor					
Tact					
Voice					

CHAPTER *10* Developing a Positive Attitude

ACTIVITY 10-3	**Foundation Skills**
Self-Improvement Plan	*Personal Qualities:* *Self-Esteem*

Objective: To develop self-esteem by choosing a personal trait and making a plan to improve that trait.

Ben Franklin wrote in his *Autobiography* about a self-improvement plan he devised. His ambition was to wipe out all his faults and arrive at perfection. To do this he made a book in which he listed the 13 virtues he thought desirable. His idea was to obtain good habits by concentrating on one virtue every week. Reflecting on the success of his self-improvement plan, Franklin wrote, "But on the whole, though I never arrived at the perfection I had been so ambitious of obtaining, but fell far short of it, yet I was, by the endeavor a better and a happier man than I otherwise should have been, if I had not attempted it. . . ."

For this activity, you will do something similar to what Ben Franklin attempted. In the previous activity you rated your personal traits. Now choose one trait you wish to improve. Then answer the questions and follow the directions below.

Make a Plan

1. Which personal trait do you wish to improve?

_____

2. Why did you choose this trait over the other personal traits?

_____

_____

3. What do you plan to do to improve this trait?

_____

_____

Check Your Progress

For a week, track your progress in breaking bad habits connected with the personal trait you chose to improve. Use the scale below to check your progress each day of the week.

How satisfied were you with each day's progress? (Circle one)

1	2	3	4	5
Very Dissatisfied				Very Satisfied

(Continued on next page)

In the space below, write a paragraph in which you tell what you learned about yourself from your week of trying to improve your personal trait. Will you need to spend more time trying to correct bad habits?

_____

_____

_____

_____

_____

_____

_____

_____

_____

_____

_____

_____

_____

_____

_____

_____

_____

_____

_____

Move On

What personal trait will you try to improve after this one? _____

_____

CHAPTER *10* Developing a Positive Attitude

ACTIVITY 10-4	**Workplace Competencies**
The Importance of Attitude	*Information:* *Interpreting and Communicating Information*

Objective: To help you see how a poor attitude can affect your relationships with your employer and your coworkers.

Lila arrived at her part-time job at the supermarket 20 minutes late. It wasn't the first time. Jan had to cover for Lila and missed her break. "Thanks very much," Jan said, barely concealing her anger when Lila finally relieved her.

"What's wrong with her?" Lila asked Bob. "She should know by now that I don't relate to clocks. That's just the way I am."

"Well," answered Bob, "she was at that checkout for four hours straight. She wasn't too happy about working even longer."

"That's right, Bob, stick up for Jan. Why don't you tell the manager while you're at it? I know how jealous you've been of me ever since I got a better grade than you in geometry."

"Lila, I don't know what you're talking about. All I know is that you were 20 minutes late."

"I can't *believe* how picky some people are! Anyway, I have a good excuse today. I had to talk with Ted. Last night I spent two hours telling him how to improve his personality, and now he says he doesn't think he wants to go out with me anymore! I only told him for his own good! Some guys are just too weak to deal with an honest person like me."

Later Lila joined some of the other cashiers on break in the back of the store. "Sharon has been showing us the sweater she bought to wear to the dance this weekend," Carol told Lila.

"You're going to wear *that* to the dance?" Lila said. Sharon put the sweater back in its bag. The other workers bit their lips and stared uncomfortably at their fingernails for some time.

Finally Carol said, "Speaking of this weekend, Lila, would you consider working for me on Saturday afternoon? Gerry's invited me to go to the beach."

"Gerry Johnson? So he finally found a girl who'd go out with him, eh? What a loser!"

Carol's face turned red with anger and embarrassment. She turned away from Lila and hurried back to work at the front of the store.

"Another person who can't stand to hear the truth! I don't know *why* I bother to try to help some people! Do they appreciate it? No! You think I *enjoy* telling them these things? It's for their own good! Why is everyone so sensitive? Do I have to be a phony like the rest of you, tip-toeing around so I won't step on anyone's poor little toes?"

As Lila was speaking, her audience gradually moved away and went back to work. Looking around and seeing that she was alone, Lila shrugged and helped herself to a soft drink.

(Continued on next page)

Later in the day one of the baggers became ill and had to go home before the end of her shift. Ms. Walters, the manager, asked Lila to close her checkout lane and help out with bagging.

"I don't know why _I_ always get picked on," Lila complained. "It's not my problem and it's not my responsibility."

"For now you'd best do as you're asked, Lila," Ms. Walters said. "And stop by to see me before you leave tonight. We need to talk."

1. Have you ever known anyone like Lila? How did this person make you feel?

_____

_____

_____

2. What do you think caused Lila to behave as she did?

_____

_____

_____

3. How could others help Lila improve her attitude?

_____

_____

_____

4. Do you think it's too late for Lila to change her attitude? Why or why not?

_____

_____

_____

5. Think about your own behavior. Have you ever been in a situation where you acted like Lila? Describe the situation.

_____

_____

_____

6. If you answered yes to question 5, what would you do to change your attitude and behavior?

_____

_____

_____

CHAPTER 10 Developing a Positive Attitude

ACTIVITY 10-5	Workplace Competencies
Being Assertive	*Information:* *Interpreting and Communicating Information*

Objective: To help you learn how to be personally effective by being assertive.

Sometime in your working life, you are likely to run into people who rub you the wrong way or try to take advantage of you. The way you handle these irritations can make a difference in your career success. It is usually best to be assertive when you need to stand up for yourself, but it is not always easy to do. Beginning workers, especially, have the tendency to come on too strong—being angry and aggressive rather than assertive.

You read in your textbook about the difference between being assertive and being arrogant or getting angry. In this activity, you will decide how to be assertive without being aggressive or arrogant.

Think of a situation where you either acted assertively or wish you had. In the space below and on the next page, write notes for a brief oral presentation. For your presentation, describe what the problem was. Tell three ways you could have reacted to the problem. Explain how you handled the problem and what happened afterwards as a result of your actions. Finally, tell what made your actions assertive rather than aggressive and why it was or would have been better to be assertive in handling this particular situation. Make your presentation to your classmates.

Describe the problem.

_____

_____

_____

_____

_____

_____

Tell three ways you could have reacted to the problem.

_____

_____

_____

(Continued on next page)

_____

_____

_____

_____

_____

_____

Explain how you handled the problem and what happened afterwards.

_____

_____

_____

_____

_____

_____

_____

Explain what made your actions assertive rather than aggressive and why assertive action was best in this situation.

_____

_____

_____

_____

_____

_____

_____

_____

CHAPTER *10* Developing a Positive Attitude

ACTIVITY 10-6

Discovering a Model for Effective Behavior

Research

Objective: To learn about actions that can help make you successful in life and work.

In his best-selling book, *The 7 Habits of Highly Effective People,* Stephen Covey explains his philosophy on how to improve personal effectiveness. The seven habits Dr. Covey suggests developing are:

1. Be proactive (take responsibility for your own life and actions).
2. Begin with the end in mind (think about the results you want in view of how you define success).
3. Put first things first (decide what is most important to you and organize your life around achieving your goals).
4. Think win/win (when interacting with another person, think of how both of you can benefit rather than just how you can win).
5. Seek first to understand, then to be understood (take time to listen—to find out what a problem is—and only then present your ideas for solving the problem).
6. Synergize (synergy means the whole is greater than the sum of its parts; it often refers to people or things working together to create a result that was beyond expectations).
7. Sharpen the saw (take care of yourself physically, spiritually, mentally, and emotionally to be at your best).

Go to your local library and locate a copy of Dr. Covey's book or some other book that suggests ways to develop good habits and positive attitudes. Use these references to answer the following questions.

1. Think of something you need or want to do. How can you be proactive in accomplishing this task?

_____

_____

_____

2. Visualize a goal and write it in the space below. Then describe proactive steps you can take to reach that goal.

_____

_____

_____

(Continued on next page)

3. Think about all the things you do in a week. Make a list of your priorities—the things that are most important to get done—and follow it for a week. Did setting priorities help you accomplish the tasks and goals you planned?

_____

_____

_____

_____

4. Think of a situation in which you had a negative interaction with another person. How could you have changed your actions to create a win/win situation for both of you?

_____

_____

_____

_____

5. Practice listening to a friend or a classmate before offering your opinion. Does listening to someone else's ideas sometimes cause you to change your mind about your own ideas?

_____

_____

_____

_____

6. Think of a situation in your school activities where synergy occurred, perhaps in a sports game where all the players pulling together made a difference. Describe the situation and why you think the "whole was greater than the sum of the parts."

_____

_____

_____

_____

7. Describe the way you take care of yourself physically, spiritually, mentally, and emotionally.

_____

_____

_____

_____

CHAPTER 11 Workplace Health and Safety

ACTIVITY 11-1

Evaluating Nutritional and Exercise Needs

Objective: To help you evaluate your nutritional and exercise needs.

To maintain good physical and mental health, you need to maintain a balanced diet and a regular exercise program. The following three tables will provide you with a guide for determining your personal exercise and energy needs for one day. The information for one day may be extended to determine your needs for weeks, months, and years.

First keep a record of everything you eat in a 24-hour period. Use Table 2 to locate each type of food you eat. Fill in the number of calories you consumed in the blank to the right of each food item. (You may need to estimate some of the portions to determine the number of calories consumed.) Then add the number of calories consumed in one day and record the total at the bottom of Table 2.

Second, compare your total calories consumed with your age, sex, weight, and height listed on Table 1. This table gives the average weight and height range for the given age groups.

Third, keep a list of all your physical activities for one day. Use Table 3 to record the estimated total energy consumed for each activity. Add the amount of energy used in one day and enter the total at the bottom of Table 3. Once you have completed these activities, answer the questions on the next page.

TABLE 1 Recommended Daily Dietary Allowances

Sex	Age	Weight	Height	Calories
Males	11–14	99 lbs.	62"	2,800
	15–18	145 lbs.	69"	3,000
	19–22	160 lbs.	70"	3,000
Females	11–14	101 lbs.	62"	2,300
	15–18	120 lbs.	64"	2,300
	19–22	128 lbs.	65"	2,000

Source: The Nutrition Almanac, 4th ed. McGraw-Hill, 1996.

(Continued on next page)

TABLE 2   Nutritional Values of Common Foods

Foods	Portions	Calories	Total	Foods	Portions	Calories	Total
Vegetables				**Soups**			
Beans, green	½ cup	20	_____	Chicken noodle	1 cup	60	
Broccoli	⅔ cup	29	_____	Beef vegetable	1 cup	70	
Cabbage, raw	½ cup	21	_____	Tomato (water)	1 cup	90	_____
Carrots, raw	1 med.	21	_____	**Beverages**			
Peas, steamed	½ cup	56	_____	Soda	12 oz.	140	
Potato, baked	1 med.	98	_____	Diet soda	12 oz.	1	_____
Sweet potato	1 med.	183	_____	Fruit drinks	12 oz.	130	_____
Fruits				Flavored waters	12 oz.	90–110	_____
Apple, raw	1 med.	76	_____				
Bananas	1 med.	88	_____	**Sugar and sweets**			
Grapefruit	½ med.	75	_____	Candy, milk chocolate	1 oz.	145	_____
Oranges	1 med.	70	_____	Honey	1 tbsp.	65	_____
Orange juice	6 oz.	90	_____	Jams and preserves	1 tbsp.	55	_____
Tomatoes	1 large	40	_____	Sugar, white	1 tbsp.	45	_____
Tomato juice	4 oz.	25	_____	**Fast foods**			
Milk products				Pizza, cheese	⅛ of 12"	240	_____
Whole milk	1 glass	124	_____	Spaghetti & meatballs	1 cup	330	_____
2 percent milk	1 glass	120	_____	Hamburger	reg.	275	_____
Cheese, cheddar	1 oz.	110	_____	Cheeseburger	¼ lb.	320	_____
Ice cream	½ cup	147	_____	Chicken fillet	reg.	495	_____
Yogurt, low-fat	8 oz.	110	_____	Roast beef sandwich	reg.	355	_____
Meat, fish, poultry				Fish fillet	reg.	440	_____
Beef, ground	3 oz.	243	_____	French fries	large	197	_____
Chicken breast	3 oz.	150	_____	Chef salad	large	309	_____
Fish, fillet	1 piece	160	_____	Seafood salad	large	168	_____
Eggs	1 large	80	_____	Apple pie	reg.	305	_____
Pork, loin	3½ oz.	130	_____	Chocolate shake	reg.	390	_____
Bread, cereals				**Fats and oils**			
Bread, white	1 slice	70	_____	Butter	1 tbsp.	100	_____
Bread, whole wheat	1 slice	70	_____	Margarine	1 tbsp.	100	_____
Oatmeal	¾ cup	132	_____	Salad dressing, blue cheese	1 tbsp.	60	_____
Rice, white	½ cup	90	_____				
Corn flakes	1 cup	100	_____	Salad dressing, French	1 tbsp.	60	_____
Wheat flakes	1 cup	125	_____	Salad dressing, Italian	1 tbsp.	70	_____
				Mayonnaise	1 tbsp.	100	_____

Total number of calories for 24 hours: _____

TABLE 3 Exercise and Energy Consumption

Activity	Calories Burned per Hour	Estimated Total Energy Consumed per Day
Basketball	360–660	_____
Bicycling	240–420	_____
Dancing	240–360	_____
Housework	240–300	_____
Mowing lawn	400–600	_____
Running	600–800	_____
Swimming	360–750	_____
Walking	300–400	_____
Relaxing or sleeping	50–100	_____
Total amount of energy consumed in one 24-hour day:		_____

Use the information from the three tables to answer the following questions.

1. Did you eat more food than is needed to maintain growth and energy for a person of your sex, age, weight, and height?

   Yes _____   No _____

2. How much more or less than the recommended number of calories did you consume?

   _____

3. How many calories did you burn in one day?

   _____

4. Subtract the number of calories burned from the total number of calories consumed from food eaten in one day. Are you now above or below the recommended number of calories needed?

   Above _____   Below _____

5. How much above or below are you from recommended amount?

   Above _____   Below _____

6. Write a brief summary of your findings with recommendations for an ideal nutritional and exercise program for yourself.

   _____

   _____

   _____

   _____

   _____

CHAPTER 11 Workplace Health and Safety

ACTIVITY 11-2	**Foundation Skills**
Planning Healthy Menus	*Personal Qualities: Self-Management*

Objective: To plan daily menus to ensure that you have a healthy diet.

In Chapter 11, you read about the need to consume healthy foods to give you energy and keep you feeling good. Use the Food Guide Pyramid in your textbook to plan a week of daily menus. Choose foods you like to eat, but also keep in mind the recommended number of servings from each food group.

Use the spaces below to write the foods you plan to eat for a week.

Day 1 _____

Food	Serving Size
_____	_____
_____	_____
_____	_____
_____	_____
_____	_____
_____	_____

Day 2 _____

Food	Serving Size
_____	_____
_____	_____
_____	_____
_____	_____
_____	_____
_____	_____

Day 3 _____

Food	Serving Size
_____	_____
_____	_____
_____	_____
_____	_____
_____	_____
_____	_____

Day 4 _____

Food	Serving Size
_____	_____
_____	_____
_____	_____
_____	_____
_____	_____
_____	_____

Day 5 _____

Food	Serving Size
_____	_____
_____	_____
_____	_____
_____	_____
_____	_____
_____	_____
_____	_____
_____	_____
_____	_____
_____	_____
_____	_____

Day 6 _____

Food	Serving Size
_____	_____
_____	_____
_____	_____
_____	_____
_____	_____
_____	_____
_____	_____
_____	_____
_____	_____
_____	_____
_____	_____

Day 7 _____

Food	Serving Size
_____	_____
_____	_____
_____	_____
_____	_____
_____	_____
_____	_____
_____	_____
_____	_____
_____	_____
_____	_____
_____	_____

CHAPTER *11* Workplace Health and Safety

ACTIVITY 11-3	**Foundation Skills**

ACTIVITY 11-3

*Responding to
Workplace Safety Issues*

Foundation Skills

*Thinking Skills:
Creative Thinking*

Objective: To learn what to do in an emergency or dangerous situation.

You work in the warehouse for a company that serves as a distributor for other companies' products. As you are walking down an aisle to count the number of boxes in a shipment of ice skates, you notice several boxes placed on the floor with a large orange arrow pointing toward the floor. The boxes all clearly state in very large print "THIS END UP AT ALL TIMES." The boxes also have the word "DANGER" printed on them and a notice saying that combustible materials are inside and that they could explode if handled improperly. You have no way of knowing how long the boxes have been sitting in this position.

Use the space below to describe the actions you would take in this situation.

_____

_____

_____

_____

_____

_____

_____

_____

_____

_____

_____

_____

_____

_____

_____

_____

CHAPTER *11* Workplace Health and Safety

ACTIVITY 11-4	**Workplace Competencies**
Causes of Accidents	*Systems:* *Understanding Systems*

Objective: To identify some causes of accidents and think of ways these accidents could be prevented.

Human error is the reason why most accidents occur. The following situations are some examples of accidents caused by human error. Read each situation and determine what caused the accident. Then tell how the accident could have been prevented. Write your answers on the lines provided. Be prepared to discuss your answers in class.

Situation 1 "I'm getting worried about Valerie," said Mrs. Hayward as she hung up the telephone. "Mrs. Myers said she left their house over two hours ago. She doesn't answer when I call her. I've even looked over by the playground, but I couldn't see her. Go see if you can find her, Mike. Tell her to come straight home."

When Mike reappeared without his sister, Mrs. Hayward became even more worried. "She's not over at the Jacksons' house. She doesn't answer when I call either," Mike said.

"Something must be wrong. This isn't like her" said Mrs. Hayward. "She knows we're going to Grandma's this evening." Mrs. Hayward waited awhile longer for Valerie to show up. Then she called the police.

The police officer pushed open the door of a vacant house at the end of the block. He could tell by the spray paint that some kids had been playing there. In the kitchen someone had left an old refrigerator. Officer Newman opened the refrigerator door. He dreaded telling Mrs. Hayward about her little girl.

1. What happened to Valerie?

_____

_____

_____

2. How could this accident have been prevented?

_____

_____

_____

(Continued on next page)

Situation 2   Mr. Porter climbed the stairs to his apartment. He had gone
downstairs for his mail after making some soup for lunch. He had
felt pretty groggy and thought a long walk in the park would do
him good. As he turned the key in his lock, he noticed the strong
smell of gas. Mr. Porter walked into the kitchen and flicked on
the light switch. He was knocked down by the explosion.

1. What was the cause of this accident?

_____

_____

_____

2. What could have prevented this accident?

_____

_____

_____

Situation 3   "How do you like this weather?" Dan asked Jess as he looked
out the window. "Snow in the middle of April! I'm just going to
bring the grill in off the patio and grill our hamburgers anyway."
  Dan placed the grill on the kitchen linoleum, poured in some
charcoal from the bag, squirted fluid on the charcoal and lit it.
When the coals were glowing nicely, he put the hamburgers on
to cook. Then he went back to the living room to play more
cards with Jess and wait for Rick to get back from the store.
When Rick came back with the groceries, he found Dan and
Jess unconscious.

1. Why were Dan and Jess unconscious?

_____

_____

_____

2. What could have prevented this accident?

_____

_____

_____

Situation 4 "Let's try a new spot this time," said Brian to his friends as they drove along the river. "That spot over there looks good. We can use that rock to dive from."

Nathan pulled the car off the road. Everyone started unloading things from the car. Brian pulled his T-shirt over his head, kicked off his shoes, and started walking toward the river.

"Aren't you going to eat first?" asked Pam.

"No, the water's too inviting," replied Brian. "Besides I want to be the first to dive from my rock."

Almost as soon as Brian plunged into the water, he felt his neck snap. Nathan and Matt floated him very carefully to shore and waited for the ambulance to arrive. Later the doctors at the hospital told Brian's parents that they were uncertain whether Brian would ever walk again.

1. What was the cause of Brian's accident?

_____

_____

_____

2. What could have prevented this accident?

_____

_____

_____

Situation 5 As Rosemary was giving the Sagans' baby a bath, the telephone started ringing. "Would you answer that!" Rosemary shouted to the twins who were watching TV downstairs. When the phone kept ringing, Rosemary left the bathroom to call downstairs for one of the boys to pick up the phone. Returning to the bathroom, she saw the baby had slipped under the water.

How could Rosemary have prevented this accident?

_____

_____

_____

_____

_____

CHAPTER 11 Workplace Health and Safety

ACTIVITY 11-5	Research
Improving Work Safety Systems	

Objective: To help you learn some proper first aid and safety procedures that may prove valuable on the job.

Even if you do not intend to work at a dangerous job, it is a good idea to be aware of job safety and first-aid procedures. For this activity, either you or your teacher will arrange for a qualified volunteer to speak to your class on job safety. The volunteer will demonstrate proper first-aid techniques. Some possible sources of volunteers are the American Red Cross, a local emergency rescue squad, or someone who specializes in occupational health and safety management.

In the space below, write three questions you would like your speaker to answer. Then think of a possible job accident, such as a mine cave-in, that you would like to know how to deal with. Write this situation in the blanks for "Possible Job Accident." Your teacher will collect these to give to your speaker ahead of time.

Question 1 _____

_____

Question 2 _____

_____

Question 3 _____

_____

Possible Job Accident

_____

_____

_____

_____

_____

_____

CHAPTER 12   Workplace Legal Matters

ACTIVITY 12-1

Analyzing Discrimination

Objective: To evaluate typical work cases to determine whether discrimination has occurred.

Case 1   You work for the Charwood Company, a construction company that builds commercial buildings. The majority of the company's employees are male. One day a coworker, Marina, approaches you and asks for your suggestions. Marina works on a construction crew and handles electrical wiring. Marina tells you that her new supervisor has asked her for a date three times. She has refused him, but lately he has become more aggressive and has started criticizing her work. Today, the supervisor gave her a negative job evaluation, which means that she will not receive a raise this year. In the past, Marina's evaluations have all been good, and her supervisors have praised her work. Marina asks you what she should do.

1. Is this company practicing discrimination because it has more male than female employees? Explain why or why not.

   _____

   _____

   _____

2. Is Marina the subject of discrimination? If so, what type?

   _____

   _____

3. What would you tell Marina to do now? Should she ignore the issue and try to stay out of the supervisor's way?

   _____

   _____

   _____

   _____

(Continued on next page)

Case 2   Ethan is a high school student who has a part-time job. He has man-
aged to save $1,200 as a down payment for a used car. The car costs
$9,600, and Ethan will need a loan to buy it. Ethan earns an average of
$100 a week. The monthly payments for the car loan would be around
$267 a month. Insurance and operating costs would add another $160
a month. After checking with a local bank, Ethan was told by the loan
officer that they would not lend him the money for the car. Ethan then
checked with a savings and loan, which says they will lend the money
if Ethan's parents will agree to repay the loan.

1. Was the bank discriminating against Ethan? Explain why or why not.

_____

_____

_____

2. If this case were changed so that Ethan is 22, has a full-time job, earns $380 a week, and is a mem-
ber of a minority group, would your answer to question 1 be different? Explain why or why not.

_____

_____

_____

Case 3   You work part-time for a fast-food restaurant. State and federal
regulations require that students cannot work beyond 11 P.M. on
school nights. Three nights this week, your supervisor has asked you
to close the restaurant at 11 P.M. and prepare it for the next day's
opening. Cleaning and putting away all food products takes about
45 minutes. The supervisor regularly asks you to close the restaurant
during the week.

1. Is this restaurant violating any law? If so, what type of law?

_____

_____

_____

2. What would you do in this situation?

_____

_____

_____

_____

CHAPTER 12 Workplace Legal Matters

ACTIVITY 12-2 *Interviewing a Lawyer*	**Foundation Skills** *Basic Skills:* *Writing and Listening*

Objective: To help you understand the different kinds of legal assistance.

As a class project, invite a lawyer to speak to your class. Use the space below to write a letter of invitation to the lawyer. In your letter, suggest a few topics your class would like to know about, such as the questions on the next page. When the lawyer visits your class, listen carefully and write answers to the questions.

Invitation Letter to Lawyer

(Date) _____

(Lawyer's Name and Address)

_____

_____

_____

(Salutation)

Dear _____ :

_____

_____

_____

_____

_____

_____

_____

(Complimentary Close) _____,

(Your Name) _____

(Continued on next page)

1. What career opportunities are there in the law?

   _____

   _____

   _____

2. What must a young person do to prepare for a career in law?

   _____

   _____

   _____

3. When should young people seek legal advice?

   _____

   _____

   _____

4. What are the costs of legal services?

   _____

   _____

   _____

5. What are the most frequent types of arrests involving young people?

   _____

   _____

   _____

6. Write one or two additional questions you would like to ask.

   _____

   _____

   _____

7. After the interview, complete this sentence: I was most interested in hearing about . . .

   _____

   _____

   _____

CHAPTER *12* Workplace Legal Matters

ACTIVITY 12-3	**Workplace Competencies**
Negotiating and Writing a Contract	*Interpersonal Skills: Negotiating to Arrive at a Decision*

Objective: To negotiate a contract and put it in writing.

A contract is a legal agreement between two or more people. When you enter into a contract, you want it to be binding. Five elements are necessary for a contract to be binding.

1. The people signing the contract must agree to its terms.
2. The signers of the contract must be legally competent (18 years old and mentally capable of understanding the terms of the contract).
3. The contract must have a legal purpose.
4. Consideration (usually money) must be given in exchange for actions agreed to in the contract.
5. The contract must be in proper legal form (date and place of the agreement, names and addresses of everyone signing the contract, purpose of the contract, amount of consideration, signatures of all parties).

An example of a short contract is shown below.

CONTRACT

On this date __May 24, 200X__ , I __Lawrence J. Chu, 1248 Mariella Court, Westerville, OH 43081,__ agree to sell to __Marissa Johnson, 842 Marston Way, Columbus, OH 43030__ the following property:

1997 Honda motorbike, serial number HMC78943212

The buyer, __Marissa Johnson__ , agrees to purchase the motorbike AS IS for a price of __$1,300.00 (one thousand three hundred dollars)__ . The buyer has inspected the property and agrees that the seller makes no warranties about the future operating condition of the property.

Signed _____   Date _____

Signed _____   Date _____

(Continued on next page)

For this activity, your teacher will assign you to work with a classmate to write a contract. In your team of two, one of you is planning to earn extra money during your summer break by painting houses. The other person on the team is a homeowner. Assume that both of you are over 18 years old. Decide who will play each role, then negotiate the price for the job. After determining a price, use the space below to write a contract. Be sure your contract includes all the elements required to make the contract legal and binding. Then answer the questions that follow.

CONTRACT

_____

_____

_____

_____

_____

_____

_____

_____

1. Is there mutual agreement between the parties to the contract?

_____

_____

2. Are the parties competent? What factors given in the case make them competent?

_____

_____

3. Is the purpose of the contract legal? _____

4. What consideration is being given?

_____

_____

5. Is the contract in proper legal form? Explain.

_____

_____

_____

CHAPTER *12* Workplace Legal Matters

ACTIVITY 12-4
Small-Claims Court

Objective: To learn about cases handled in small-claims court and the procedures for filing claims.

The U.S. legal system gives people several ways to resolve legal disputes. One of these ways is the small-claims court. Disputes brought before this court involve relatively small amounts of money. Settling an issue in small-claims court saves the cost of hiring a lawyer to represent you, a cost that could be greater than the amount in dispute.

For this activity, you are to find out about your local small-claims court. To do that, find the name of the legal official (often an appointed magistrate) who handles small-claims cases and set up an interview. Use the interview to get answers to the questions below. Get permission from the official to observe some small-claims hearings. Then write a description of the procedures followed by the magistrate and the parties involved.

Name of magistrate _____

Telephone number _____

Date/time of interview _____

Location of interview _____

1. What is the largest amount of money involved that will be accepted for a small-claims dispute? the smallest?

   _____

2. What should a person do to try to settle an issue before taking it to small-claims court?

   _____

   _____

   _____

3. How does a person start a small-claims action? Describe the process.

   _____

   _____

   _____

(Continued on next page)

4. If you bring a case to small-claims court and you do not like the decision, what else can you do?

_____

_____

_____

5. Use the following space to describe the procedures the magistrate and the people involved in the cases followed during your observations.

_____

_____

_____

_____

_____

_____

_____

_____

_____

_____

_____

_____

_____

_____

_____

_____

_____

_____

_____

_____

CHAPTER 13 Interpersonal Relationships at Work

| ACTIVITY 13-1 | **Foundation Skills** |

ACTIVITY 13-1
Coworker Case Studies

Foundation Skills

*Thinking Skills:
Problem Solving*

Objective: To learn about typical interpersonal problems between coworkers and how to handle similar situations in your own job.

On this page and the next are several case studies involving relationships between coworkers. Read each case study carefully. Then answer the questions that follow it. After you have completed this activity, you should have a better idea of how to develop and maintain good relationships with all your coworkers.

Case 1   Ted is enrolled in a work-education program. Each morning he attends a work-related class, and in the afternoon he works in a clothing store. One day last week, Ted learned how to install the tape in the cash register. The next day he heard one of the salesclerks say that the cash register was not working properly. Another salesclerk attempted to fix the machine but was unsuccessful.

Ted approached the two clerks and said, "I think I can fix it."

One of them remarked, "What do you know about cash registers?"

Annoyed by the remark and feeling confident of his ability to fix the machine, Ted said, "I'll show you how to fix it!" He pushed his way in front of the salesclerks, opened the cash register side panel, rethreaded the machine, and punched the "no sale" key. The machine operated properly, and the receipt came out. Ted, feeling he had proven a point, walked back to his own work area without saying a word.

Did Ted prove a point? How will this situation affect his future relations with coworkers?

_____

_____

_____

Case 2   Kayla, who just recently graduated from high school, works for a magazine publisher. She has been working at her new job as a data-entry clerk for only two weeks. On her coffee breaks, Kayla likes to go down to the composition department and watch Juan and Karen use the computers to makeup magazine pages. Juan has even volunteered explanations on how the programs work. Karen has never offered to explain anything to Kayla. Yesterday Karen told Juan that she had to take special classes to learn the software programs, so she didn't think it was right for Juan to teach Kayla how to use the software. "Besides," Karen said, "she might get so good that she'll take over one of our jobs!"

(Continued on next page)

If you were Juan, how would you answer Karen?

_____

_____

_____

Case 3 Janine began her first job as an assembler in a large manufacturing firm. Lois, one of the other assemblers, was especially friendly to Janine. They began to spend all their coffee breaks together. Lois was a gossip, and everyone knew it. Although Janine did not gossip, she listened to Lois talk about everyone else in the department. Janine soon noticed that many of the workers were beginning to be very cool and distant toward her, which was exactly the way they treated Lois.

If you were Janine, how would you have handled your relationship with Lois and with the other workers in the department?

_____

_____

_____

Case 4 Like most people, Walt likes to receive a pat on the back for a job well-done. But his supervisor seldom makes favorable remarks about Walt's work. Carlos is very careful about his work, and he receives many compliments from the supervisor. Carlos takes the compliments well and is not resented by other employees, except Walt. After watching the supervisor compliment Carlos for doing a fine job on a difficult project, Walt said to Carlos, "I suppose you think all that butter will get you a raise." Carlos looked up, said nothing, and continued his work. Walt went on, "Too good to talk with me, huh? Now that you and the boss are so buddy-buddy, I guess you can't associate with the rest of us."

1. What is the reason for Walt's behavior?

_____

_____

2. If you were Carlos, what would you do or say?

_____

_____

3. How can you accept compliments on your work and still maintain good relationships with your coworkers?

_____

_____

CHAPTER 13 Interpersonal Relationships at Work

ACTIVITY 13-2	**Foundation Skills**
Personal Effectiveness	*Thinking Skills: Reasoning*

Objective: To increase your personal effectiveness by learning to observe and understand others.

To deal effectively with others, you have to understand them. To understand other people, you must listen to what they say as well as pay attention to such clues as body language and personality traits. See if you can discover in the following case studies how observing others can help you develop your personal effectiveness.

Case 1 Mario is a sales representative who sells building materials for Green's Construction Company. He loves the contact with other people and the challenge of his sales job. Mario's boss, Mr. Green, is a temperamental man. Many of the employees have difficulty communicating with him. Mario, however, is always able to present his thoughts or problems to Mr. Green with positive results.

This morning Mario had a problem involving a lumber shipment to a construction site. He walked into the Green Construction Company office and noticed that Mr. Green was standing by himself. Mr. Green's shoulders were slouched forward, and his hands were on his hips. Mario did not present his problem. Instead he decided to postpone it until after lunch.

1. Why did Mario decide to wait to inform Mr. Green of his problem?

_____

_____

_____

_____

2. When would be a good time to approach Mr. Green? Why?

_____

_____

_____

_____

(Continued on next page)

Case 2 Sulinn and George are placement counselors in an employment agency. George is the supervisor of the counseling section. He has developed most of the procedures for matching jobs with applicants and making referrals. Sulinn has shown some resentment toward following the procedures George has outlined. In fact, she seldom smiles or shows any interest in George's work. During the past six months, Sulinn has never complimented George for his efforts. Recently she had an argument with George on how placement referrals are made.

Sulinn has been studying methods of placement since she became unhappy with existing procedures nearly a year ago. She has finally developed a method that is, indeed, superior to the one now used. However, when Sulinn placed a carefully typed proposal for the new procedure on George's desk, he closed his lips tightly and only partly read it. Then he dropped the proposal in his desk drawer. No further discussion on the proposed placement procedure took place.

1. Why wasn't Sulinn's proposal given fair consideration?

_____

_____

2. If you were Sulinn, what would you have done differently?

_____

_____

Case 3 Ann Thach is a sales representative for a company that specializes in publishing career-education textbooks for high schools. She regularly calls on career-education teachers. Ann's job is to persuade teachers to order textbooks for their classes.

Ann recently called on Mrs. Thornton, who is the director of career education for the high schools in a midwestern city. Ann greeted Mrs. Thornton with a cheerful, "Good afternoon, how are you?"

Mrs. Thornton snapped, "Oh, just fine," emphasizing the word "fine." Rather than showing Mrs. Thornton the career-education materials she brought, Ann visited with Mrs. Thornton for a few minutes, then invited her to dinner that evening. Mrs. Thornton accepted.

Ann spent the remainder of the afternoon showing new products to teachers in the high schools.

1. Why didn't Ann begin discussing the career-education products with Mrs. Thornton that afternoon?

_____

_____

2. When should Ann try to get an order for career-education materials from Mrs. Thornton? Why?

_____

_____

CHAPTER **13** Interpersonal Relationships at Work

ACTIVITY 13-3	**Foundation Skills**
Improving Your Personal Traits	_Personal Qualities: Self-Management_

Objective: To apply a four-step process for improving personal traits.

In Chapter 13, you read about a four-step process for self-improvement. The four steps are to focus on one trait at a time, draw up a plan and stick to it, keep track of your progress, and move on to another trait that needs improvement after you've made progress toward improving the first one.

Choose a personal trait that you would like to improve, then use the spaces below to create a plan and monitor your progress.

Personal Self-Improvement Plan

Step 1: Zero in on one trait at a time.
What trait do you want to improve first? _____

Step 2: Draw up a plan and stick to it.
In the space below, list the actions you will need to take to improve. For example, if you think you'll need regular reminders to help you improve, include in your list writing notes to yourself and placing them where you'll see them often. Or you might want to ask friends to give you reminders.

_____

_____

_____

_____

_____

_____

_____

_____

_____

_____

_____

(Continued on next page)

Step 3: Keep track of your progress.

Use the spaces below to identify how you will measure your progress. For example, if you're trying to improve your study habits, you might use better grades as a measure of progress. List all the ways you plan to use to evaluate your improvement.

_____

_____

_____

_____

_____

_____

_____

_____

Step 4: Move on.

Decide when you will know you're ready to move on to another area of self-improvement and describe that point below. For example, if you're trying to improve your writing skills, you might feel that you've made the progress you want when your writing assignments are graded and returned with no corrections. Be specific about your goal. Then choose a new trait for your next plan of improvement.

_____

_____

_____

_____

_____

_____

_____

_____

Next trait to improve: _____

CHAPTER *13* Interpersonal Relationships at Work

ACTIVITY 13-4

Developing Interpersonal Skills

Workplace Competencies

Interpersonal Skills: Participating as a Member of a Team

Objective: To identify and improve interpersonal skills by working as a member of a team.

For this activity, your teacher will assign you to a team of four or five. Each team is to choose a career area and prepare an advertising campaign whose aim is to attract students to that career. Your advertising campaign might consist of posters, flyers, newspaper ads, and so on.

Here are the activities that you will need to complete as a team:

1. Choose a career to feature in your campaign.
2. Research the career area to find ideas about what to include in your advertising.
3. Discuss ideas for promoting this career.
4. Analyze tasks that need to be done.
5. Make team assignments.
6. Prepare the advertising materials.
7. Present your campaign to the class.

After presenting your advertising campaign, answer the following questions.

1. What interpersonal skills did you use to choose a career area?

_____

_____

2. If you had disagreements or a conflict about how to develop your advertising campaign, how did you resolve the conflict?

_____

_____

3. How would you rate yourself as a team member? Did you take a leadership role, or did you follow another team member's lead? Were you cooperative, or did you go off to do your own thing?

_____

_____

4. Do you think the other people on your team would rate you the same as you rated yourself?

_____

_____

CHAPTER *13* Interpersonal Relationships at Work

ACTIVITY 13-5
Learning About Workplace Diversity

Objective: To learn about the cultural differences among people who make up the work force.

Figure 13.3 in your textbook shows the projected growth in the U.S. population by ethnic group. Within these broad groups are many other groups who share similar traditions and attitudes. For example, Asian is a broad category that has several subgroups, such as Chinese, Japanese, Korean, and Vietnamese.

For this activity, choose an ethnic group to research. During your research, you'll find things that are common to all people, but your goal is to identify differences that will help you to understand and appreciate the cultural diversity of the people around you. Among topics to research are special holidays, traditions, communication styles, geographic areas of greatest population, and values.

Your research might include reading reference materials in the library or interviewing people from different ethnic groups. Use your research to answer the following questions.

Group researched _____

1. What are some special holidays or celebrations observed by this group?

_____

_____

2. What are some traditions that are different from those followed by other ethnic groups?

_____

_____

3. How do communication style(s) differ?

_____

_____

4. Where do most people in this group live?

_____

5. What are the primary values?

_____

_____

CHAPTER **14** Teamwork and Leadership

ACTIVITY 14-1	**Foundation Skills**
Leadership Evaluation	*Thinking Skills: Decision Making*

Objective: To help you rate your own leadership behavior and skills.

The following self-rating activity will provide an opportunity for you to evaluate your leadership behavior and skills. Be honest with yourself and try to be as objective as possible when responding to the following 30 items. Record your response in the blank at the left of each question using the number code below.

Points
3—Most of the time
2—Usually
1—Seldom
0—Never

_____ 1. When working with others, can you be influenced (changed) by them?

_____ 2. Can you get others to change their goals?

_____ 3. Can you adapt to different people and conditions?

_____ 4. Do you avoid assuming that other people think like you?

_____ 5. Can you avoid judging others by their appearance only?

_____ 6. Are you willing to let your group take credit for things you accomplished?

_____ 7. Do you compliment others for outstanding achievement?

_____ 8. Do you try to make others feel important?

_____ 9. Can you spot hidden meanings when you communicate with others?

_____ 10. Do you make a special effort to encourage individuals in your group?

_____ 11. Are you willing to listen to others' ideas?

_____ 12. Do you listen attentively to others?

_____ 13. Are you aware of other people's moods?

_____ 14. Do you carefully analyze problems before taking action?

_____ 15. Are you embarrassed by your group members' glaring errors in grammar?

_____ 16. Do you recognize the needs of others?

_____ 17. Do you go out of your way to become better acquainted with associates?

_____ 18. Do you maintain eye contact when talking with someone?

_____ 19. Do you avoid directing your attention to a person's physical defect?

(Continued on next page)

_____ **20.** Do you make a special effort to recognize classmates when outside the school setting?

_____ **21.** Can you refrain from calling attention to other people's limitations?

_____ **22.** Do you avoid bragging about yourself?

_____ **23.** Can you resist arguing with a very argumentative person?

_____ **24.** Can you overlook minor annoyances?

_____ **25.** Are you careful not to "pass the buck"?

_____ **26.** Do you avoid complaining about things you cannot control?

_____ **27.** Can you resist repeating information given to you in confidence?

_____ **28.** Can you avoid making negative remarks about others?

_____ **29.** Do you walk and stand in a dignified manner?

_____ **30.** Can you resist showing bias in public?

Checking Results

If you have been honest with yourself, a score of 60 points should indicate you have developed good leadership qualities. If you scored below 30 points, consider the areas that need self-improvement.

In the space below, list your leadership qualities that need improving. Write a paragraph on how you can improve them.

_____

_____

_____

_____

_____

_____

_____

_____

_____

_____

_____

_____

_____

CHAPTER **14** Teamwork and Leadership

ACTIVITY 14-2	**Foundation Skills**
Parliamentary Procedure	*Thinking Skills: Reasoning*

Objective: To help you become familiar with the types of motions used in meetings.

To be effective as a meeting participant, you need to know the meanings of parliamentary terms. Fill in the blank with the term listed below that best completes each sentence. If necessary, refer to Figure 14.4 in your text to review the terms.

quorum	bylaws	call to question	minority	new business
amend	minutes	unfinished business	motion	agenda
second	convene	table	adjourn	aye

1. A motion to _____ temporarily postpones making a decision on an issue.

2. The minimum number of members who must be present for the group to conduct official business is a _____ .

3. A motion to _____ changes another motion.

4. _____ is a topic brought before the members for at least the second time.

5. The items or topics to be addressed at a meeting are listed on a(n) _____ .

6. An official request for a group to take action or reach a decision is a(n) _____ .

7. A motion to _____ ends a meeting.

8. Items or topics brought before the group for the first time are _____ .

9. A _____ is a request by a member for the group to vote on a motion.

10. To _____ is to call a meeting to order.

11. _____ govern an organization's operation, including electing officers, determining membership qualifications, and setting meeting times.

12. A motion to _____ shows approval of a motion made by another member of the group.

13. Saying _____ is a formal way of saying yes.

14. The _____ of the meeting provide a written record of what is said and done during the meeting.

15. A _____ is less than half the voting members at a meeting.

CHAPTER **14** Teamwork and Leadership

ACTIVITY 14-3

Analyzing Parliamentary Procedure

Foundation Skills

Thinking Skills: Reasoning

Objective: To learn how to apply some basic rules of parliamentary procedure.

Conducting meetings properly is necessary in the working world. As a leader, you want to give everyone a chance to speak during a meeting. You also want to cover everything you intended to discuss. The rules of parliamentary procedure help groups conduct meetings in an orderly way. Think of these rules as you read the two cases below. Write your answers to the case questions in the spaces provided. Check with your teacher to verify your responses.

A. A motion has been made that the Taylorsville Community Group participate in the community's "Toys for Tots" fund-raising campaign. You are the chairperson.

1. What type of motion is this? _____

2. After some discussion, a member calls the motion to question. What will you do?

   _____

3. If someone else seconds the motion, what does that mean?

   _____

4. If the meeting lacks a quorum, can this motion be passed at this meeting? Why or why not?

   _____

5. If a majority of the members vote aye on this motion, what will you do?

   _____

B. A motion has been made that the Springfield DECA Club sell candy at the holiday basketball tournament. The motion has been seconded, discussed, and a vote taken. It carried and the chairperson is ready for other items of business. You, a member, look at your watch and find it is almost time for afternoon classes to begin. What would you do to end the meeting?

1. What motion is required? _____

2. Does it need a second? _____

3. What type of vote is needed to carry the motion? _____

CHAPTER **14** Teamwork and Leadership

ACTIVITY 14-4	**Workplace Competencies**
Supervisor Case Studies	*Interpersonal Skills:* *Exercising Leadership*

Objective: To learn how to handle supervisory problems.

At some time in your future career, there's a good chance that you will have to supervise workers. A supervisor needs to know how to communicate effectively with others and how to delegate responsibility. Read the following case studies, then answer the questions. As you read these cases, think about the skills and traits being exercised by the supervisors. Which skills and traits lead to success as a supervisor, and which do not?

Case 1   Frank Garcia is the supervisor of the mail-order department of a large store. Every evening after the store closes, Frank checks over the orders written by the six order clerks and compiles a report on the total mail-order sales. Lowell, one of the order clerks, volunteered to help Frank by checking the orders during the day at times when he wasn't busy. Frank refused Lowell's offer, even though it meant Frank had to work overtime for nearly two hours every night.

1. Why do you think Frank refused Lowell's offer of help?

_____

_____

_____

2. If you were Frank, how would you organize the work load?

_____

_____

_____

Case 2   Nancy Nichols is the head nurse in the surgical ward of a hospital. She often works 50 or 60 hours a week. Much of the work is emotionally demanding. When things are going well for Nancy, she is quite lenient with the staff. When Tom, a student nurse, was ten minutes late one morning, Nancy shrugged and said, "Don't worry about it." One morning the next week, Tom was just two minutes late. Nancy was tired and worried about one of the patients. She threatened to have Tom expelled from the training program if he were late again. Tom was confused by Nancy's sudden change in attitude. Many of the other nurses who work with Nancy have had similar experiences.

(Continued on next page)

1. Why is Nancy's behavior so confusing to those who work for her?

_____

_____

_____

2. If you worked for Nancy, how would you react to her behavior?

_____

_____

_____

3. Can you think of any actions Nancy might take to become a more effective supervisor?

_____

_____

_____

Case 3   As the operations manager for a small plastics firm, Hector Bloom was always busy. He was responsible for seeing that the temperature in the offices was comfortable, that the parking lot was cleared of snow, and that the remodeling of the president's office proceeded on schedule. Hector's job covered everything from getting light bulbs changed to preparing for a major addition to the building. On most days Hector would get to the office early and make up the day's assignments for his workers. Because he had so many things on his mind, the assignments weren't always clear. By the time the workers arrived, Hector was usually in a meeting or otherwise unavailable. When he returned to his office, he became angry that many of the jobs he had assigned either had been done incorrectly or had not been done at all.

1. What is Hector Bloom's main supervisory problem?

_____

_____

_____

2. What solutions can you think of to this problem?

_____

_____

_____

CHAPTER **14** Teamwork and Leadership

ACTIVITY 14-5
Portrait of a Leader

Objective: To identify traits and skills that a leader possesses.

   Is a person born with a gift for leadership, or can leadership skills be learned? What makes one person a leader and another a follower? For this activity, you are to select a well-known person whom you consider to be a leader and find out more about his or her leadership style.

   First, read a biography or autobiography of the person. After reading the book, use the space below to write a brief description of the person. Then answer the questions that follow.

Name of leader _____

Description _____

_____

_____

_____

_____

_____

_____

_____

_____

_____

_____

_____

_____

_____

(Continued on next page)

1. What qualities made this person a leader?

   _____

   _____

   _____

2. How did this person develop his or her own style of leadership?

   _____

   _____

   _____

3. How did the person learn from her or his mistakes?

   _____

   _____

   _____

4. Who was a positive influence on this person during childhood?

   _____

   _____

   _____

5. What qualities do you admire most about this person?

   _____

   _____

   _____

6. What do you consider this person's weaknesses?

   _____

   _____

   _____

7. What image does the leader project?

   _____

   _____

   _____

CHAPTER **15** Professional Communication Skills

ACTIVITY 15-1	**Foundation Skills**
Speaking Skills	*Basic Skills: Speaking*

Objective: To learn how to evaluate your own speaking skills.

How you speak will probably have a great influence on your success in the working world. Your aim should be to express yourself clearly. One way to do this is to think about your purpose before you speak. Are you speaking to inform, to persuade, or to entertain?

Another way to express yourself clearly is to organize your thoughts. This is especially important in formal speeches. Some basic patterns you can use are enumeration, generalization with example, cause and effect, and comparison and contrast. These patterns are described in Figure 15.2 of your text. For this activity, you are to compose a well-organized, three- to five-minute speech with the purpose of either speaking to inform or speaking to persuade.

If you are speaking to inform your audience, tell about one of these topics:

- A decision you had to make
- A job interview you had
- An emergency someone handled
- Your part-time job or work as a volunteer

If you are speaking to persuade, choose one of these topics:

- Why (choose a place) is a good place to live
- Why (choose a career) is a good career choice
- Why someone should buy (choose a product)
- Why (pick a company) should hire you
- Why (choose a school, college, apprentice program, or branch of the military) is a good school or training program after graduation

Before you present your speech to the class, use a tape recorder to record your speech. Play back the tape and use the following questions to evaluate your speaking skills. Make notes for those items you need to work to improve.

Content

1. Did I inform or persuade? _____

2. Was the speech well-organized? _____

3. Was there an easily identified pattern to my speech? _____

4. Did I stick to the subject? _____

5. Was my speech interesting? _____

(Continued on next page)

Voice Quality

1. Did I use pleasant pitch? _____

2. Was my voice relaxed? _____

3. Was my voice neither too loud nor too soft? _____

4. Did I use varied inflections? _____

Speaking Habits

1. Was my pronunciation correct? _____

2. Did I enunciate correctly? _____

3. Did I vary my rate of speed? _____

4. Did I use standard English? _____

Personal Comments

1. What weaknesses did I notice in my speech?

_____

_____

_____

_____

_____

_____

2. What should I do to improve my speech?

_____

_____

_____

_____

_____

_____

CHAPTER *15* Professional Communication Skills

ACTIVITY 15-2	**Foundation Skills**
Listening Skills	*Basic Skills: Listening*

Objective: To help you develop good listening skills.

Being a good listener involves more than just hearing the sounds of words. To be a good listener, you need to concentrate so that you understand the speaker's message. This activity is designed to help you develop your concentration skills.

On the following two pages are two sets of word lists. All of the words in each item are related in some manner, except for one word. As you listen to the words in each item, you are to choose the word that does not belong with the other words. For example, if your partner reads, "a. banana, b. apple, c. grape, d. carrot," you should choose "d" since carrot is a vegetable, while the other words in that item are fruits.

You are to pair up with another student in class to do this activity. For the first half of the activity, student 1 is to read Word List 1 to student 2, who is to listen and circle his or her answers on the Answer Sheet for Word List 1 (on page 168). Then, student 2 is to read Word List 2 to student 1, who will circle his or her answers on the Answer Sheet for Word List 2.

When you are the person doing the reading, you are to read the words for each numbered item only once. When you are finished with the activity, check your answers with your teacher.

Word List 1

1. a. oak   b. maple   c. apple   d. rose   e. pine

2. a. house   b. condominium   c. apartment   d. church   e. mobile home

3. a. symphony   b. cymbals   c. flute   d. cello   e. violin

4. a. daybreak   b. sunrise   c. dawn   d. aurora   e. dusk

5. a. robin   b. meadowlark   c. sparrow   d. wasp   e. bluejay

6. a. hockey   b. ballet   c. football   d. basketball   e. wrestling   f. skiing

7. a. priest   b. mechanic   c. photographer   d. camera   e. psychologist   f. electrician

8. a. bus   b. sled   c. taxi   d. truck   e. van   f. car

9. a. lantern   b. candle   c. match   d. lamp   e. flashlight   f. chandelier

10. a. fern   b. daisy   c. tulip   d. lilac   e. lily   f. orchid

11. a. brake   b. windshield   c. steering wheel   d. battery   e. tailpipe   f. automobile
    g. accelerator

12. a. saw   b. grinder   c. router   d. can opener   e. belt sander   f. drill   g. sledgehammer

13. a. cow   b. sheep   c. tiger   d. pig   e. horse   f. turkey   g. chicken

14. a. bass   b. trout   c. catfish   d. halibut   e. crab   f. tuna   g. salmon

15. a. Michigan   b. New Hampshire   c. Detroit   d. Massachusetts   e. Texas
    f. Florida   g. Washington

16. a. hate   b. love   c. jealousy   d. ecstasy   e. fear   f. depression   g. anger   h. death

17. a. poodle   b. coyote   c. cocker spaniel   d. collie   e. Irish setter   f. terrier
    g. golden retriever   h. beagle

18. a. furniture   b. chair   c. table   d. bed   e. dresser   f. couch   g. footstool   h. desk

19. a. parrot   b. grasshopper   c. mosquito   d. gnat   e. tick   f. bee   g. ant   h. fly

20. a. red   b. burgundy   c. maroon   d. scarlet   e. vermilion   f. orange   g. crimson   h. ruby

Word List 2

1. a. lemon   b. lime   c. orange   d. peach   e. radish

2. a. whale   b. spider   c. dog   d. cat   e. cow

3. a. canoe   b. kayak   c. raft   d. rowboat   e. barge

4. a. river   b. stream   c. creek   d. water   e. pond

5. a. soldier   b. sergeant   c. general   d. captain   e. private

6. a. window   b. door   c. building   d. floor   e. wall   f. ceiling

7. a. George Washington   b. John Hancock   c. Thomas Jefferson   d. Abraham Lincoln   e. Theodore Roosevelt   f. Ronald Reagan

8. a. nephew   b. uncle   c. aunt   d. father   e. brother   f. son

9. a. summer   b. winter   c. fall   d. season   e. autumn   f. spring

10. a. sage   b. cinnamon   c. parsley   d. dill   e. pickle   f. oregano

11. a. cold   b. frigid   c. icy   d. sultry   e. chilly   f. freezing   g. frosty

12. a. diamond   b. gold   c. ruby   d. emerald   e. sapphire   f. amethyst   g. garnet

13. a. noun   b. verb   c. phrase   d. adjective   e. adverb   f. preposition   g. pronoun

14. a. law   b. surveyor   c. doctor   d. judge   e. painter   f. actress   g. bus driver

15. a. contents   b. chapter   c. unit   d. index   e. appendix   f. book   g. foreword

16. a. Earth   b. Venus   c. Mercury   d. Plymouth   e. Pluto   f. Mars   g. Saturn   h. Jupiter

17. a. decade   b. year   c. time   d. hour   e. day   f. week   g. minute   h. month

18. a. waiter   b. hostess   c. customer   d. cashier   e. cook   f. busboy   g. dishwasher   h. restaurant manager

19. a. carpenter   b. plumber   c. lawyer   d. electrician   e. plasterer   f. iron worker   g. laborer   h. assembler

20. a. goblet   b. paper plate   c. tumbler   d. wine glass   e. teacup   f. coffee mug   g. beer stein   h. paper cup

(Continued on next page)

Answer Sheet for Word List 1

1. a b c d e
2. a b c d e
3. a b c d e
4. a b c d e
5. a b c d e
6. a b c d e f
7. a b c d e f
8. a b c d e f
9. a b c d e f
10. a b c d e f

11. a b c d e f g
12. a b c d e f g
13. a b c d e f g
14. a b c d e f g
15. a b c d e f g
16. a b c d e f g h
17. a b c d e f g h
18. a b c d e f g h
19. a b c d e f g h
20. a b c d e f g h

Answer Sheet for Word List 2

1. a b c d e
2. a b c d e
3. a b c d e
4. a b c d e
5. a b c d e
6. a b c d e f
7. a b c d e f
8. a b c d e f
9. a b c d e f
10. a b c d e f

11. a b c d e f g
12. a b c d e f g
13. a b c d e f g
14. a b c d e f g
15. a b c d e f g
16. a b c d e f g h
17. a b c d e f g h
18. a b c d e f g h
19. a b c d e f g h
20. a b c d e f g h

CHAPTER **15** Professional Communication Skills

<table>
<tr><td>**ACTIVITY 15-3**
Writing a Memo</td><td>**Foundation Skills**
Basic Skills:
Writing</td></tr>
</table>

Objective: To practice writing a memo.

    Memos are most often used for correspondence between people who work for the same company. Occasionally a memo may be sent to people outside the company who work closely with employees. Only one topic is usually covered in a memo.

    For this activity, write your own memo in response to the memo below and the letter on the next page. Read the memo below first, then follow the directions.

MEMORANDUM

TO: Georgia Lewellen, Vice President, Human Resources
FROM: Joyce A. Heart, Accounting
DATE: March 29, 200X
SUBJECT: Changes in Hiring Practices

I will be unable to attend the management meeting on Friday. I understand that you will be discussing a possible change in the company's procedures for screening and hiring job applicants.

As a department head, I have always felt that I should be able to interview applicants and make the final decision on who is hired to work in this department. Will this be possible in the future, or will the human resources office continue to interview and hire workers for all departments?

Write your answers to the following questions.

1. What do you know about the reader of the above memo?

2. What was Joyce Heart's main purpose in writing the memo—to inform, request, confirm, persuade, inquire, or complain?

3. What is the subject of the memo?

(Continued on next page)

Before answering Joyce Heart's memo, read the following memo.

TRIUMPH TOY COMPANY
342 Madison Avenue
New York, NY 10001

INTEROFFICE MEMORANDUM

TO: Jack Wolfe, Vice President, West Coast Region
FROM: Georgia Lewellen, Vice President, Human Resources
DATE: February 20, 200X
SUBJECT: Changes in Hiring Practices

After considerable discussion with our attorneys, I am pleased to announce certain changes in hiring practices for the company. The changes in policy are summarized as follows:

- The human resources department for each division will screen applicants for all open positions.
- The HR department will explain to all applicants the screening tests currently in use and will administer those tests to all applicants regardless of age, gender, or race.
- The HR department will ensure that every applicant has an opportunity to take the screening tests within normal business hours.
- At least three candidates (or more when available) will be referred to the appropriate department head for interviewing after the screening process.
- Following each interview, the department head will write a brief summary of the interview and file it with the human resources department.
- The department head will make the final selection of the best candidate for the job.

A complete copy of this new policy is being prepared now and will be sent to all offices within the next few days. If you have any questions before you receive the written policy, please call me.

Answer these questions about the memo above.

4. What do you know about the reader of the memo?

_____

5. What is the main purpose of the memo—to inform, request, confirm, persuade, inquire, or complain?

_____

Now imagine that you are Georgia Lewellen. Using the memo in Figure 15.5 of your textbook as your model, write your response to Joyce Heart's memo. Use the spaces below.

MEMORANDUM

TO: _____

FROM: _____

DATE: _____

SUBJECT: _____

_____

_____

_____

_____

_____

_____

_____

_____

_____

_____

_____

_____

_____

_____

_____

_____

CHAPTER **15** Professional Communication Skills

ACTIVITY 15-4	**Workplace Competencies**
Writing Business Letters	*Information:* *Using Computers to Process Information*

Objective: To practice writing effective business letters.

Writing effective business letters is a skill that you'll be able to use both in your personal life and in your career. Business letters are written for many different situations. For example, you might write a letter of application when applying for a job or a letter to a customer responding to a customer service issue. In this activity, you are to read about two different business situations and then write business letters appropriate for each situation. Refer to Figure 15.6 in your textbook for an example of a properly prepared business letter.

Situation 1 You ordered new stereo headphones over the Internet from a firm in another state. When your new headphones arrived, they did not work properly. The sound was fine in the left side, but the right side would not work at all. Write a consumer complaint letter to the company describing the problem and what you would like the company to do. Make up the name and address of the company. Before you write the letter, answer the following questions. Then use the space on the next page to write your letter. Be sure to use appropriate business letter format.

1. Who is your reader?

   _____

   _____

2. What is your purpose—to inform, request, confirm, persuade, inquire, or complain?   `

   _____

3. What is the subject of your letter?

   _____

   _____

Letter for Situation 1

_____

_____

_____

_____

_____

_____

_____

_____

_____

_____

_____

_____

_____

_____

_____

_____

_____

_____

_____

_____

_____

_____

_____

_____

(Continued on next page)

Situation 2   Suppose that you are interested in attending a particular school after you graduate from high school. If you already know the school you want to attend, use that one. If not, look through college and trade school catalogs and directories in your local library or ask your counselor about them.

Write a letter to the school you want to attend. Ask your counselor or teacher to show you some sample *school information request* letters. Address your letter to the school's Office of Admissions. Ask for an application and a general information bulletin, along with information on financial aid. In your letter tell what date you will graduate from high school, your planned major or subjects of interest, and when you plan to enroll.

Before you write your letter, answer the following questions. Then use the space on the next page to write your school information request letter.

1. Who is your reader?

_____

_____

2. What is your purpose—to inform, request, confirm, persuade, inquire, or complain?

_____

3. What is the subject of your letter?

_____

_____

Letter for Situation 2

_____

_____

_____

_____

_____

_____

_____

_____

_____

_____

_____

_____

_____

_____

_____

_____

_____

_____

_____

_____

_____

_____

CHAPTER 15 Professional Communication Skills

ACTIVITY 15-5
Analyzing Effective Speakers

Objective: To view videos of effective speakers and determine the techniques and skills that make them effective.

Through your study of history, you've learned about some major political and government leaders. Many of these people have also been inspiring speakers. Some names that come to mind are John F. Kennedy, Martin Luther King, Jr., Ronald Reagan, and Barbara Jordan. People from other occupations are also good speakers. Think about talk-show host Oprah Winfrey, who speaks throughout her program and maintains the interest of her audience.

For this activity, you are to view videos of people making speeches. Your local library should have selections of famous speakers or other videos, such as self-improvement videos, from which you can choose. View a few videos, then choose a speaker whom you believe to be especially effective. Study the speaker's style and skills, then answer the questions below.

Speaker's name _____

_____

1. What was the subject of the speech? _____

2. What organizing techniques did the speaker use? _____

_____

3. What was the speaker's purpose? Was that purpose achieved by the speech? Explain why or why not.

_____

_____

_____

4. If the speaker's purpose was to persuade, how effective was the speaker?

_____

5. What qualities of this speaker caused you to select her or him as an effective speaker?

_____

_____

_____

_____

CHAPTER 16 Thinking Skills on the Job

ACTIVITY 16-1	**Foundation Skills**

Reading Skills:
Fact and Opinion

Basic Skills:
Reading

Objective: To learn to distinguish between fact and opinion in your reading.

When you are reading, it's a good idea to identify statements of fact and statements of opinion. Statements of fact are not always true, but they can be proven true or false. Statements of opinion are based on someone's personal feelings about something and cannot be proven true or false. For example, "The American Revolution began in 1590," is clearly wrong. This statement of fact is one you can prove to be false by checking historical documents. "The American Revolution was our country's most glorious war," is an opinion. You may agree with this opinion, but you can't prove that the American Revolution was more glorious than the Civil War, for instance.

Read the following sentences. In the blank beside each sentence, place "O" if the sentence is a statement of opinion. Place an "F" in the blank if it is a statement of fact.

_____ 1. Recipes that include the word "Florentine" in the title will have spinach as one of the ingredients.

_____ 2. The Culinary Institute of America in Hyde Park, New York, is the best cooking school in the United States.

_____ 3. Thomas Edison invented the light bulb.

_____ 4. The Sahara Desert is the largest desert on Earth.

_____ 5. Antoine de Saint Exupery wrote, "It is only with the heart that one can see rightly; what is essential is invisible to the eye."

_____ 6. At the end of the Philadelphia concert, singer Art Powers announced that the donations had topped $40 million.

_____ 7. *Braveheart* is the finest adventure movie ever made.

_____ 8. The toughest course in high school is physics.

_____ 9. Seattle is a good city to work in.

_____ 10. State transportation officials stated that an accident occurs about once a minute on state roads.

_____ 11. The only thing that matters is winning.

_____ 12. The quarterback suffered a stiff neck during last Friday night's game.

_____ 13. Dining is a special event at The Greenhouse.

_____ 14. Abraham Lincoln was our greatest president.

_____ 15. John Kennedy was our thirty-fifth president.

_____ 16. Senior citizens deserve respect.

CHAPTER **16** Thinking Skills on the Job

ACTIVITY 16-2	**Foundation Skills**
Looking for Problems	_Thinking Skills:_ _Reasoning_

Objective: To identify actual or potential problems in work situations.

When you begin work, you will likely encounter problems both large and small. How you handle the problems will determine how well you succeed in your work. The first step in the problem-solving process you read about in Chapter 16 is to identify and clarify the problem. You first have to understand what the problem is before you can decide how to solve it.

For this activity, read each of the short cases, then identify the problem and the issues involved.

Case 1   John Flores tries to make a good impression on the job. He wears clean, neatly pressed suits and follows good grooming habits. Since he works as a salesperson, he has frequent contact with customers. John believes that his professional appearance alone should help him make sales, and he sometimes loses patience with customers who say they are "just browsing." John's coworker, Jason Martin, also works as a salesperson. Jason favors a more casual look and sometimes wears rumpled clothing. His approach to customers is also more casual than John's. Jason offers to answer customer questions and get any information they need. Unlike John, Jason studies new products and how they work so he will be able to answer questions. As the sales supervisor, you have a goal of improving sales. Jason's sales are better than John's, but both could be improved.

1. What is the problem?

_____

_____

_____

2. How would you solve the problem?

_____

_____

_____

_____

_____

Case 2 "I can't help noticing that Rick has been very irritable lately," said Jessica. "For example, when I asked him if he needed any help with inventory, he just snapped, 'What's the matter? Don't you have enough to do?'"

1. What is the problem?

_____

_____

_____

2. How would you solve the problem?

_____

_____

_____

_____

_____

Case 3 You work for a chain of local convenience stores. Your store manager has just sent a memo to all the store employees explaining that groups of teenagers have been coming into the stores late in the evening. While a couple of them distract the worker on duty, the others pick up items and walk out the door without paying for them. Most of the stores have only one person working the evening shift. The manager wants store workers to be especially watchful when large groups enter the store during the evening hours.

1. What is the problem?

_____

_____

_____

2. How would you solve the problem?

_____

_____

_____

_____

_____

CHAPTER 16 Thinking Skills on the Job

ACTIVITY 16-3

Learning to Think Creatively

Foundation Skills

Thinking Skills:
Creative Thinking

Objective: To expand your creative ideas through brainstorming.

Many entrepreneurs have been able to build new businesses by identifying a market need and coming up with creative ideas to meet the need. Large corporations also value creativity in employees who solve problems or think of new products.

For this activity, your teacher will assign you to a team of four or five students. With your team, choose a problem (perhaps an issue in school government or a goal of getting your school connected to the Internet) and then think of alternatives for solving the problem. Use the methods for creative thinking described in your textbook chapter (brainstorming, associating ideas, creating models, suggesting analogies, questioning assumptions, applying logic). Answer the following questions to describe the problem and possible solutions.

1. What is the problem your team chose to solve?

_____

_____

2. In evaluating alternatives, what methods to inspire creative thinking did you use? Circle each method below that you used, and describe how you used it.

Brainstorming

_____

_____

_____

_____

Associating Ideas

_____

_____

_____

_____

Creating Models

_____

_____

_____

Suggesting Analogies

_____

_____

_____

Questioning Assumptions

_____

_____

_____

Applying Logic

_____

_____

_____

3. What alternatives seem the best solutions to the problem? Why?

_____

_____

_____

_____

_____

CHAPTER 16 Thinking Skills on the Job

| ACTIVITY 16-4 | **Workplace Competencies** |

ACTIVITY 16-4
Knowing How to Use Resources

Workplace Competencies
Resources:
Allocating Material and Facility Resources

Objective: To learn how to allocate space for a work area.

In some jobs, you might be responsible for deciding how to use the physical space in a store or some other business. In your textbook chapter, you read about Maria, who works at SuperSounds. Maria has done her job well and has been asked to suggest ideas for creating a new display space. For this activity, assume that you are Maria. You are to plan a new room that will be used for demonstrating stereo equipment. Read the description of the space and the products to display, then plan how you will allocate space for each item.

The Display Space
The area set aside for the new display is drawn below, along with the dimensions of the room.

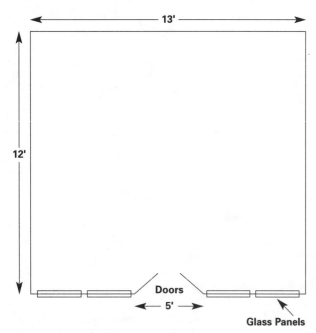

The Equipment
Four shelving units will be needed to display the stereo units and speakers. Each shelving unit measures 24 inches deep by 48 inches wide. Space will be needed for customers to sit and listen to the different stereo equipment. Decide how many chairs to place in the room. Each chair will require a space 24 inches by 24 inches.

Some of the larger stereo speakers will not fit on the shelving units and will need to stand on the floor. Four sets of large speakers need to be on display. Each set of speakers requires a floor space roughly 2 feet by 3 feet.

Planning the Space

Using the dimensions of the room and equipment given, draw your plan for how to arrange the new listening room. The grid below has a scale of one square equal to one square foot. After drawing the plan, answer the questions on the next page.

(Continued on next page)

1. Were you able to fit all the equipment into the room?

   _____

2. What special considerations did you have to take into account in deciding how to place equipment?

   _____

   _____

   _____

3. Did you use the decision-making process to help you evaluate needs and weigh options? If so, describe how you used it.

   _____

   _____

   _____

   _____

   _____

4. What special skills did you use in solving this problem? Describe each skill and how you used it.

   _____

   _____

   _____

   _____

   _____

CHAPTER *16* Thinking Skills on the Job

ACTIVITY 16-5	**Research**
Problem Solving	

Objective: To work with a team to brainstorm and develop creative alternatives for solving a problem.

For this activity, your teacher will assign you to a team of four or five students. Your class has been chosen to make suggestions for ways to raise money for new band uniforms. Each team is to follow the problem-solving process described in Chapter 16 and develop suggestions for raising funds.

To complete the activity, you will need to research various alternatives for raising money. In researching alternatives, ask people you know what items they would buy as part of a fund-raising effort. Use the spaces below to analyze the problem and write your answers for each step in the process. When you are finished, present your findings to the class. As a class, you may want to vote on the most creative solution to the fund-raising problem.

1. Identify and clarify the problem. (Describe the issues.)

_____

_____

_____

_____

2. Generate alternative solutions. (Use research to prepare a list of possibilities. Describe each.)

_____

_____

_____

_____

_____

_____

_____

_____

(Continued on next page)

3. Evaluate the probable consequences of the solutions. (Describe the potential for success in raising money with each of your possible solutions.)

_____

_____

_____

_____

_____

4. Decide on the best solution. (Describe your solution and the reasons why you chose it.)

_____

_____

_____

_____

_____

5. Implement the solution. (Describe how you would put your solution into play.)

_____

_____

_____

_____

6. Evaluate the results. (Describe the measures you would use to evaluate the results.)

_____

_____

_____

_____

_____

CHAPTER **17** Technology in the Workplace

ACTIVITY 17-1
Calculating Time and Wages

Objective: To calculate time, weekly time worked and the related wages.

In this activity, you will calculate the total time worked in one week by each of four employees. *If you have a calculator, use it for this activity.* After you have totaled the time for each employee, multiply the hours by the rate to get the total wages.

There are two special considerations in this activity:

1. Calculate time to the **nearest quarter-hour each day.** If an employee works an extra 7 to 14 minutes beyond the hour or quarter-hour, give the person credit for a full quarter-hour. This is the case on Wednesday and Thursday for Carmen Fisher—whose time card is shown below. If an employee is short of a full hour's work by only a few minutes, there is no penalty—and there are no penalties for any of these employees this week.

2. Any employee who works more than 40 hours in any week is paid 1½ times his or her usual rate for the overtime worked beyond 40 hours. In the example below, Carmen Fisher worked 40½ hours. She would be paid 40 hours at $10 per hour and one-half hour at $15 per hour.

Time Card

Week Ending _October 5_____

Employee No. _23-74-412_____

Name _Carmen Fisher_____

DAY	IN	OUT	IN	OUT	TOTAL
MON	8:00	12:02	1:01	5:00	*8*
TUE	7:58	11:59	1:00	5:05	*8*
WED	8:02	12:05	1:00	5:07	*8¼*
THU	8:00	12:05	1:01	5:08	*8¼*
FRI	7:58	12:03	1:04	5:05	*8*
SAT					
SUN					

Total Time _*40½*_____ **Hours**

Rate Per Hour _$10_____

Total Wages _*$407.50*_____ (incl. ½ hr. OT)

(Continued on next page)

Total the hours worked and calculate the total wages for each employee.

Time Card

Week Ending May 9

Employee No. 97-76-512

Name George Baker

DAY	IN	OUT	IN	OUT	TOTAL
MON	7:00	11:01	12:00	4:01	
TUE	6:59	11:00	11:59	4:04	
WED	7:01	11:03	12:00	4:01	
THU	7:00	10:59	12:00	4:02	
FRI	7:01	11:02	12:01	4:01	
SAT					
SUN					

Total Time _____ **Hours**

Rate Per Hour $10

Total Wages _____

Time Card

Week Ending May 9

Employee No. 54-63-784

Name Marilyn Gaines

DAY	IN	OUT	IN	OUT	TOTAL
MON	8:00	12:01	1:00	4:00	
TUE	8:01	11:00	—	—	
WED	9:02	12:02	1:03	5:01	
THU	8:01	12:00	1:01	4:01	
FRI	9:00	12:02	1:00	3:01	
SAT					
SUN					

Total Time _____ **Hours**

Rate Per Hour $16.50

Total Wages _____

Time Card

Week Ending _May 9_____

Employee No. _32-96-132_____

Name _Carl Rexroad_____

DAY	IN	OUT	IN	OUT	TOTAL
MON	9:01	12:00	1:01	5:01	
TUE	8:03	12:01	1:03	5:06	
WED	8:04	12:04	1:02	5:08	
THU	8:03	12:02	1:01	5:06	
FRI	8:05	12:06	1:04	5:05	
SAT					
SUN					

Total Time _____ **Hours**

Rate Per Hour _$10.50_____

Total Wages _____

Time Card

Week Ending _May 9_____

Employee No. _32-64-813_____

Name _Darrel Clark_____

DAY	IN	OUT	IN	OUT	TOTAL
MON	9:01	11:00	—	—	
TUE	9:00	12:02	1:00	5:00	
WED	8:00	12:00	1:00	4:01	
THU	9:01	11:59	—	—	
FRI	8:00	12:01	—	—	
SAT					
SUN					

Total Time _____ **Hours**

Rate Per Hour _$12_____

Total Wages _____

CHAPTER **17** Technology in the Workplace

ACTIVITY 17-2	**Foundation Skills**
Using a Calculator	*Basic Skills: Mathematics*

Objective: To learn to use a calculator correctly.

Employers value workers with good math skills. While you may be able to use a calculator or a spreadsheet program on the job, you still need to understand how to set up and solve math problems. Since calculators are so common today, your employer will most likely expect you to know how to use one correctly. In this activity, you will practice using a calculator. First, study the illustration below to review the keys on a typical calculator. You may also want to review the operating instructions for the calculator you plan to use to complete this activity.

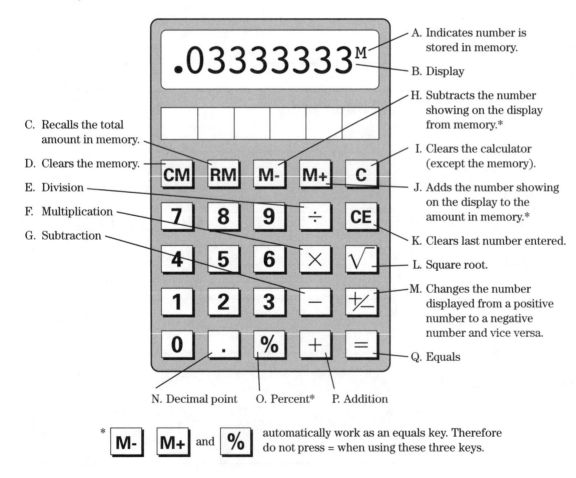

A. Indicates number is stored in memory.

B. Display

C. Recalls the total amount in memory.

D. Clears the memory.

E. Division

F. Multiplication

G. Subtraction

H. Subtracts the number showing on the display from memory.*

I. Clears the calculator (except the memory).

J. Adds the number showing on the display to the amount in memory.*

K. Clears last number entered.

L. Square root.

M. Changes the number displayed from a positive number to a negative number and vice versa.

N. Decimal point   O. Percent*   P. Addition

Q. Equals

* **M-** **M+** and **%** automatically work as an equals key. Therefore do not press = when using these three keys.

Correcting a Key-Press Error

If you have entered the wrong number in the calculator, you can correct this by pressing the [CE] key and then entering the number you intended. For example, try entering 6 + 7 + 6 + 7 + 7 in the calculator. The last 7 was a mistake so press [CE] and enter 6 instead. Press the = key. Your total should be 32. Remember to press [C] to clear the calculator before correcting the errors in the following problems.

_____ 1. Enter 1043.25 [+] 88.19 [+] 42.11. Instead of 42.11, you intended to enter 42.01. Correct your error and write your answer in the blank.

_____ 2. Enter 998 [−] 38.7. Instead of 38.7, you wanted to enter 387. Correct your error and write your answer in the blank.

_____ 3. Enter 87 [×] 244. You intended to enter 442 instead of 244. Write your correct answer in the blank.

_____ 4. Enter 774 [÷] 9. You intended to enter 777 instead of 774. Correct your error and write your answer in the blank.

Basic Math Operations

Before using the calculator to solve each of the following problems, estimate your answers. Write your estimate on a piece of scratch paper. Then write in the answer displayed on your calculator for each problem.

Addition

1.	2.	3.
10 13 15 10 8 +13	1784 1463 +2582	66.44 28.36 59.73 +34.82

Subtraction

1.	2.	3.
95 −26	5989 −4162	48.670 −23.567

Multiplication

1.	2.	3.
56 ×28	793 ×897	11.46 ×11.2

Division

1. 3)1365   2. 56)49112   3. .25)100

(Continued on next page)

Expressing Fractions in Decimal Form

To convert fractions to decimal form, divide the numerator (top number) by the denominator (bottom number). Use your calculator to express the following fractions as decimals. Write the answer displayed on your calculator on the blank provided in front of each fraction.

1. _____ $\frac{1}{4}$ **2.** _____ $\frac{9}{16}$ **3.** _____ $\frac{56}{88}$

Memory Calculations

You will probably want to use the memory operations of your calculator when you have several totals to add together to find a grand total. Take a look at the two examples below. One shows the calculations done by hand. The other shows the same calculations done by the calculator's memory operations.

By hand

2.50		8.40		17.35	
4.00		2.60		+14.75	
8.60		+3.75		32.10	GRAND TOTAL
+2.25		14.75	TOTAL		
17.35	TOTAL				

On a calculator

2.50 + 4 + 8.60 + 2.25 [M+] Display 17.35ᵐ [C] 8.40 + 2.60 + 3.75[M+] Display 14.75ᵐ. Press the [RM] key for the grand total. Display 32.1ᵐ. Press [CM] to clear memory. Then press [C] to clear the calculator.

Use the memory in your calculator to do the following calculations. First find the sum for each addition problem like in the example above. Then press [RM] to receive the total of all of the sums. Write your answers in the appropriate places below.

1.	2.31	**2.**	3.10	**3.**	3.04	**4.**	3.64	**5.**	3.18
	4.58		3.92		4.77		4.10		6.33
	7.12		5.14		5.82		6.39		8.51
	38.11		41.20		44.01		46.12		31.14
	6.50		3.85		5.30		6.50		4.10
	21.10		7.80		6.36		8.30		+25.12
	+3.00		+5.30		+20.14		+6.00		
	TOTAL		TOTAL		TOTAL		TOTAL		TOTAL

GRAND TOTAL _____

Percent Problems

Using your calculator can save you time when you need to do various percentage problems in business. Each of the following business problems involve percentages. Read the directions. Then solve the problems with your calculator.

Commission

To figure how much commission you should be paid on $1500 if you receive a 10 percent commission, enter 1500 [×] 10 [%] Remember that you do not press the [=] key. The display will read 150, which you should interpret as $150. Calculate the amount of commission for the following:

1. 15% of $3200 = _____

2. 25% of $800 = _____

3. 20% of $7500 = _____

Interest

To calculate interest on a loan of $6500 at 8 percent to be paid off in three years, enter 6500 [×] 8 [%] [×] 3 [=]. The display will read 1560, which means $1560 is the amount of interest.

Calculate the amount of interest for the following:

1. a loan of $3400 at 9.6 percent _____

2. a loan of $65,000 at 12 percent for 15 years _____

3. a loan of $150,000 at 15 percent for 30 years _____

Sales Tax

To figure the total price of an item costing $43.50 with a 5 percent sales tax, enter 43.50 [+] 5 [%]. 45.675 will be displayed, meaning the total cost will be $45.68.

Figure the total prices for the following:

1. an item costing $78 with a 6 percent sales tax _____

2. an item costing $2000 with a 5 percent sales tax _____

3. an item costing $110.50 with a 6 percent sales tax _____

If you wish to know the specific amount of sales tax for the item costing $43.50 above, enter 43.50 [×] 5 [%]. The display will read 2.175, meaning the sales tax is $2.18.

Calculate the amount of sales tax for the three items under "Sales Tax" above. Write your answers in the blanks provided.

4. _____ **5.** _____ **6.** _____

(Continued on next page)

Discounts

To calculate the total price of an item costing $50 with a 20 percent discount, enter 50 [−] 20 [%]. The display will then read 40, meaning the total price is $40.

Figure the total prices for the following:

1. an item costing $24.50 with a 15 percent discount _____

2. an item costing $65.0 with a 50 percent discount _____

3. an item costing $180 with a 20 percent discount _____

Combination Discount and Sales Tax

To figure the total price of something costing $225 with a 25 percent discount and a 4 percent sales tax, enter 225 [−] 25 [%] [+] 4 [%]. The display will read 175.5, meaning $175.50.

Figure the total prices for the following:

1. an item costing $890 with a 20 percent discount and a 6 percent sales tax

_____

2. an item costing $21.95 with a 10 percent discount and a 4 percent sales tax

_____

3. an item costing $192.25 with a 30 percent discount and a 5 percent sales tax

_____

CHAPTER 17 Technology in the Workplace

ACTIVITY 17-3	Workplace Competencies
Calculating Commissions and Interest	*Technology: Applying Technology to Task*

Objective: To practice solving percentage problems involving commissions and interest.

You had some practice figuring commissions and interest when you used the calculator to solve percentage problems in Activity 17-2. Although you might expect to use a calculator for solving the majority of percent problems on the job, it's also a good idea to understand how to set up a spreadsheet to calculate such problems. Use a spreadsheet program to calculate percentages for the two sets of problems given below. Then answer the questions that follow. When calculating interest, assume that you will pay interest on the full price each year, although this would not usually be the case.

If you do not have access to a spreadsheet software program, complete this activity using a calculator.

Bud's Auto Dealership—January Sales

Salesperson	Percent Commission	Monthly Sales
Sasha Grinoff	20%	$25,000
Beth Jones	25%	$26,400
Ivan Gutierrez	30%	$11,350

1. How much commission will Sasha Grinoff receive for January sales? _____

2. How much commission will Beth Jones receive? _____

3. What will Ivan Gutierrez receive in commission? _____

City Bank Auto Loans

Automobile Price	Annual Percent Interest	Loan Period
$8058	7.5%	4 years
$5799	7.7%	3 years
$3300	10.9%	2 years

4. What is the amount of interest you would pay if you bought the first car listed above?

_____

5. What is the amount of interest you would pay if you bought the second car listed above?

_____

6. What is the amount of interest you would pay if you bought the last car listed above?

_____

CHAPTER 17 Technology in the Workplace

Research

ACTIVITY 17-4
*Choosing Computer
Hardware and Software*

Objective: To compare characteristics of several brands of personal computers and various types of software to develop a buying guide for your needs.

Computers and software are an integral part of business activities. Knowing how to evaluate hardware and software features is an important skill that will help you succeed in your work. For this activity, you are to prepare a table comparing hardware features and prices. You are to prepare a second table comparing software. Since the sources of information on both personal computers and software will probably be similar, plan to research both at the same time.

Selecting Hardware

First, decide which computers you will consider. If you are not already familiar with the models currently on the market, visit several computer stores. Observe demonstrations of new models, ask questions, read the advertising brochures. Browse through some computer magazines, too. Next, use the Buyer's Guide on the next page to write in the names and models, prices, characteristics, and special features of each personal computer. Finally, considering your own real or imagined purpose for buying a computer, indicate with a check mark (✓) which is the best buy for your purpose.

Selecting Software

Although there are many types of software available for personal computers, in this activity you are to find out what kinds of business software can be purchased.

While visiting the computer store to check out personal computers, also ask questions about software. Use the chart on page 198 to gather information on what the company or source offers for the following programs: (1) presentation, (2) database, (3) spreadsheet, and (4) desktop publishing.

When you have completed both the hardware and the software charts, compare your information with the information the rest of the class has gathered. Discuss which products would make the best buys for a small-business owner.

Buyer's Guide to Personal Computers

Company/Model	Source	Price	Processor	Memory	Hard Drive	Monitor	Special Features

(Continued on next page)

Buyer's Guide to Business Software						
Software Type	**Publisher**	**Title**	**Version**	**Source**	**Price**	**Special Features**
Presentation						
Database						
Spreadsheet						
Desktop Publishing						

CHAPTER *18* Time and Information Management

ACTIVITY 18-1	**Foundation Skills**
Using Time Honestly	*Personal Qualities: Integrity/Honesty*

Objective: To apply personal qualities of integrity and honesty to on-the-job situations.

Using time wisely not only helps you accomplish your personal goals, it also makes you a better employee. Employers value people who are self-starters and know how to organize their time to meet deadlines and to handle routine work activities. Check your own attitudes toward time by reading each of the short cases below and answering the questions.

Case 1 Evie works for a large company that develops software programs. The normal work week is 40 hours, from 9 to 5, with an hour off for lunch. Evie is a technical writer who writes the documentation manuals that explain the software and how to use it. The company recently started allowing its technical writers to telecommute three days a week. Evie decided to telecommute. On her days at home, Evie organizes her work around her baby daughter's schedule. Since the baby sleeps until 8:30 A.M., Evie works from 6:30 to 8:30 A.M., then dresses and feeds the baby. Back at work by 9:30 A.M., Evie is able to put in another three hours. From 12:30 to 2, Evie is again busy with the baby. From 2 o'clock on, she usually works until 5:30 or 6 P.M.

1. How many hours a day is Evie working?

_____

_____

_____

2. Since Evie is not working the hours from 9 to 5, is she being fair to her employer? Explain.

_____

_____

_____

Case 2 Jansen also works for the computer software company as a technical writer. Like Evie, he works at home three days a week. Jansen spends a lot of time at his computer. He usually starts working at 9 A.M. and is sometimes still at his computer at 9 P.M., with short breaks during the day. Jansen likes to keep up with what is happening on the

(Continued on next page)

Internet, so he usually logs on first thing in the morning and sometimes spends three hours surfing the Net. After lunch, Jansen starts
his work of writing the manuals. Around 5 P.M., he checks the Internet
again and also reads his e-mail messages for the day and then sends
return messages. Most of his e-mail is from friends who are also computer buffs.

1. How many hours a day is Jansen working?

_____

_____

2. Is Jansen giving his employer an honest day's work? Explain.

_____

_____

_____

Case 3   Jennifer works for the software company as a software tester. As the
programmers work on a new product, Jennifer takes the latest ver-
sion and tests to make sure it operates as intended. Since most of her
work is done at a computer, Jennifer also telecommutes three days a
week. Jennifer still owes money on her college loans, and now that
she spends more time at home she has taken on a freelance job for
another software developer. Depending on deadlines, Jennifer juggles
the hours she spends on each program. She is careful, though, to keep
a time log and makes sure she spends 40 hours a week for her
employer. Sometimes those hours may be 8 P.M. to midnight if she is
working on her freelance project. The freelance project is a software
program similar to the one she is testing for her employer. Jennifer's
employer is not aware of her second job.

1. Is Jennifer being honest in the number of hours she works for her employer? Explain.

_____

_____

_____

2. Is Jennifer demonstrating integrity by working two jobs to pay off her college loans?

_____

_____

3. Do you see any problem with the type of second job Jennifer chose? Explain.

_____

_____

_____

CHAPTER 18 Time and Information Management

ACTIVITY 18-2
Analyzing Your Time

Objective: To improve your time management skills by analyzing how you spend your time.

Do you sometimes wonder what happens to your time? Many people have this problem. You can learn how to accomplish the things you want, though, by learning how you actually spend your time.

For this activity, you are to keep a record of what you do for a week. Include all activities, such as eating, sleeping, commuting to and from school or to a job, studying, attending class, and social activities. At the end of the week, analyze your time log and answer the questions on the next page.

Time Log

Activities: **Time Consumed:**

Day 1 _____

_____   _____

_____   _____

_____   _____

_____   _____

Day 2 _____

_____   _____

_____   _____

_____   _____

_____   _____

Day 3 _____

_____   _____

_____   _____

_____   _____

_____   _____

(Continued on next page)

Name _____ **Date** _____

Class _____ **Instructor** _____

Activities: **Time Consumed:**

Day 4 _____

_____   _____

_____   _____

_____   _____

_____   _____

Day 5 _____

_____   _____

_____   _____

_____   _____

_____   _____

Day 6 _____

_____   _____

_____   _____

_____   _____

_____   _____

Day 7 _____

_____   _____

_____   _____

_____   _____

_____   _____

1. What activities did you spend most of your time doing? The least time?

_____

2. Which activities could you have omitted to save time?

_____

3. How could you have used your time more efficiently?

_____

_____

CHAPTER *18* Time and Information Management

ACTIVITY 18-3	**Workplace Competencies**
Setting Priorities	*Resources:* *Allocating Time*

Objective: To prioritize activities and learn to manage your time more efficiently.

You read in your textbook chapter about setting priorities so you can make sure you have enough time to finish tasks that are most important. For this activity, use the time log you created for Activity 18-2. In the left column below, make a list of the things you regularly do, plus the activities you want to accomplish during the next week. Also add any goals you want to work toward but can't finish in a week. In the right column, rewrite your list by priority.

List of Tasks/Activities

_____

_____

_____

_____

_____

_____

_____

_____

_____

_____

Prioritized List of Tasks/Activities

_____

_____

_____

_____

_____

_____

_____

_____

_____

_____

After setting your priorities, use the space on the next page to allocate your time for the next week. Review your plan as the week progresses, and make adjustments as needed in how you use your time. Explain how having a plan and setting priorities helped you accomplish more of the things you wanted to do.

_____

_____

(Continued on next page)

Weekly Schedule

Time	Sun.	Mon.	Tues.	Weds.	Thurs.	Fri.	Sat.
A.M. 6:00							
6:30							
7:00							
7:30							
8:00							
8:30							
9:00							
9:30							
10:00							
10:30							
11:00							
11:30							
Noon 12:00							
P.M. 12:30							
1:00							
1:30							
2:00							
2:30							
3:00							
3:30							
4:00							
4:30							
5:00							
5:30							
6:00							
6:30							
7:00							
7:30							
8:00							
8:30							
9:00							
9:30							
10:00							
10:30							
11:00							
11:30							
12:00							

CHAPTER 18 Time and Information Management

ACTIVITY 18-4
Checking Out Aids for Time and Information Management

Objective: To learn about resources to help you learn to use your time more efficiently.

Time management is a big business for some companies. Training companies are in business to train workers to manage time better. Other businesses sell products intended to help people use time more efficiently. These products include day planners, computer software programs, and video and audio tapes offering time management suggestions. Numerous books have been written promoting time management techniques.

Information management also has its share of attention. Several devices exist to help you manage information. For example, you might use a personal digital assistant (PDA) to create an address/telephone/e-mail file for people you contact frequently. Personal information management software programs are also available to help you organize and manage information.

For this activity, you are to research time and information management resources and make a list of items that you might use to improve your own time management skills. For each item, include a brief description of what it does.

Time and Information Management Resources

Books and Magazines

_____

_____

_____

CDs and CD-ROMs

_____

_____

_____

Videotapes

_____

_____

_____

(Continued on next page)

Time Management Courses/Seminars (check local college offerings as well as seminar businesses)

_____

_____

_____

Calendars/Day Planners

_____

_____

_____

Software and Electronic Devices, such as PDAs

_____

_____

_____

Use the resources you researched to answer these questions.

1. Which of the resources do you plan to use to improve your time and information management skills?

_____

_____

_____

_____

2. List five suggestions or techniques offered by the resources for improving time management.

_____

_____

_____

_____

_____

_____

_____

_____

CHAPTER 19 Economics and the Consumer

ACTIVITY 19-1

Reviewing the
Consumer Price Index

Objective: To read a graph to draw conclusions about the Consumer Price Index.

As you read in your textbook chapter, the Consumer Price Index measures changes in the prices of consumer goods and services. This index is used as a measure of inflation, which is a period when prices are rising sharply.

The graph below shows annual changes in the Consumer Price Index from 1970 to 1995. For comparison, changes in the prices of fuel oil for the same period are also included. Study the graph, then answer the questions that follow.

Annual Percent Change in Consumer
Price Indexes: 1970 to 1995

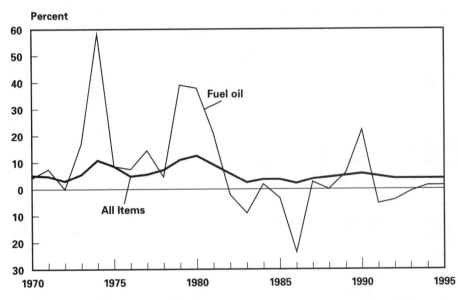

Source: Statistical Abstract of the United States, 1996, *U.S. Government Printing Office.*

1. What year shows the largest increase in prices for fuel oil? What do you think could have caused this increase?

   _____

   _____

2. What year showed the highest level of prices for all items of the Consumer Price Index? How might this level relate to inflation?

   _____

   _____

3. Did prices increase or decrease from 1994 to 1995? _____

CHAPTER **19** Economics and the Consumer

ACTIVITY 19-2	**Foundation Skills**
Buying a Used Car	*Thinking Skills: Decision Making*

Objective: To apply the decision-making process to a consumer buying decision.

Just about every young person is eager to buy a car. Since a car is expensive to buy and to operate, you should have a buying plan before making a purchase. You may even want to start saving money and planning for a car before you are eligible for a driver's license.

In Chapter 19 of your text you read about the free-enterprise economy and the role consumers play in the marketplace. For this activity, you will take the role of a consumer who wants to buy a used car. You'll apply the seven steps of the decision-making process that you learned earlier in the course. Use this decision-making process to evaluate the type and features of the car you want. As you recall, Step 1 of the decision-making process is to define your needs or wants. Using the space below, write your answers to each question within the steps of the decision-making process.

Step 1: Identify your needs and wants.

What do you want to buy? _____

Step 2: Analyze your resources.

Decide how much money you will need to spend. Before shopping for a car, you would make any necessary loan arrangements with a bank, credit union, or savings and loan association.

How much money do you plan to spend for your used car? _____

Step 3: Identify your choices.

Decide on the type of car you want. _____

1. Do you want a small, medium, or large car? _____

2. What make of car do you want? _____

3. Do you want a four-door or two-door, an SUV, sedan, or hatchback? _____

4. Do you want automatic or manual transmission? _____

5. What size engine are you looking for? _____

6. What year car do you want? _____

7. What other features would you like your used car to have? _____

Step 4: Gather information on your choices.

If you were actually buying a car, you would compare several according to such things as cost, condition, insurance, and warranty. It is wise to learn the retail book price of the car's make, year, and model. This information can be found at libraries and online. Information on used car models and how to buy a used car is included in *Consumer Reports Buying Guide,* a book available at most public libraries. Obtain the retail book price for the car you wish to inspect. Write your information below.

Car make _____   Year _____   Model _____

Retail book price $ _____   Accessories $ _____   Total price $ _____

Step 5: Evaluate your choices.

The next step is to examine the car. Use the checklist on this page and the next. The checklist will give you practice in inspecting used cars and, thus, help you in buying your first car. The best time to inspect a car is during the day when the sunlight is bright enough to make any defects visible.

Inspection of Car

A. Exterior

☐ Yes **1.** Has the car been wrecked?
☐ No   Observe surfaces of the car in sunlight; repaired surfaces can be seen by looking at the surfaces from a view almost parallel with the painted surface.

☐ Yes **2.** Is the car dented?
☐ No   Damage to bumper, grill, or painted surface reduces the value.

☐ Yes **3.** Is the paint in good condition?
☐ No   Faded paint with rust spots means the car has not been garaged. Examine lower surfaces below doors and bumpers for rust spots.

☐ Yes **4.** Do the doors fit properly?
☐ No   A door out of line may indicate the car has been involved in a wreck or that the handle/catch is defective.

☐ Yes **5.** What is the condition of the tires?
☐ No   Tires with ⅛" or less tread will soon need to be replaced. Tires worn irregularly indicate the alignment needs adjustment. A badly worn ball-joint suspension may be the cause, and a repair job would cost hundreds of dollars.

☐ Yes **6.** Are the shock absorbers good?
☐ No   A car that continues to bounce after being pushed up and down probably needs new shocks.

☐ Yes **7.** Is the glass in the windshield and doors in good condition?
☐ No   Roll the windows up and down and check for chipped edges on the glass.

☐ Yes **8.** Does the car appear to be level when empty?
☐ No   A car that tilts to one side or to the front or back probably needs new springs.

B. Interior

☐ Yes **1.** Are the brake and accelerator pedals badly worn?
☐ No   Worn pedals generally mean the car has been driven many miles.

☐ Yes **2.** Is the steering-wheel paint worn off in spots?
☐ No   If paint has been worn off the wheel, the car probably has been driven more than 50,000 miles. If the wheel is newly painted, the meaning is the same.

(Continued on next page)

☐ Yes **3.** What is the condition of the
☐ No   doorsills and armrests?
              Excessive wear here means
              excessive use.

☐ Yes **4.** What is the condition of the
☐ No   carpets and seats?
              Depressions on the seat cushions
              indicate much use. New carpets
              and seat covers are sometimes
              installed to make the car sell, but
              they indicate that the car has had
              rough use.

☐ Yes **5.** Do the door-glass mechanisms
☐ No   work smoothly?
              The windows of wrecked cars
              often are difficult to raise or
              lower.

☐ Yes **6.** Does the indicated mileage seem
☐ No   to be correct when compared with
              inside wear?
              Although it is illegal, odometers
              (instruments for measuring
              mileage) can be changed or reset.

C. Engine

☐ Yes **1.** Does the radiator show signs of
☐ No   leakage, or does the coolant
              appear dark red?
              Either condition can cause addi-
              tional repair bills.

☐ Yes **2.** Is the oil dipstick free from rust
☐ No   or sludge, and is the oil clean?
              A rusty dipstick can be serious.
              The engine may have an inside
              gasket leak or a cracked block
              that contaminates the oil. Black
              oil may indicate additive treat-
              ments that have been added to
              quiet the engine.

☐ Yes **3.** Is the oil on the automatic
☐ No   transmission dipstick clean and
              odorless?
              Dirty, bad-smelling oil can mean
              excessive transmission wear.
              Repair can be very costly.

☐ Yes **4.** Does the engine start easily, run
☐ No   smoothly, and have no unusual
              knocks when accelerated?
              If the answer is yes, the engine is
              probably not badly worn.

☐ Yes **5.** Is there a warranty date on the
☐ No   battery?
              Batteries over three years old may
              need replacement.

☐ Yes **6.** Is the exhaust system in good
☐ No   condition?
              A leaky muffler or exhaust pipe is
              dangerous and is also expensive
              to replace.

☐ Yes **7.** Does the engine or transmission
☐ No   leak?
              If oil spots appear on the parking
              area after driving, the engine and
              transmission should be checked
              for serious leaks.

D. Driving Inspection

☐ Yes **1.** Does the car steer properly?
☐ No   A car that pulls to one side of the
              road should be carefully checked.
              Free play in the steering wheel
              when the car is in motion may
              indicate the need for costly repair.
              This is especially true if the car
              has power steering.

☐ Yes **2.** Is there an increase of body noise
☐ No   and rattles on rough roads?
              Noises and rattles can signal prob-
              lems in the steering mechanism or
              the suspension system.

☐ Yes **3.** Is there any vibration or unusual
☐ No   noise on the open road at speeds
              above 40 miles per hour?
              A rear-axle hum or transmission
              noise can mean expensive repairs.

☐ Yes **4.** Is the automatic transmission
☐ No   operating properly?
              A transmission that is noisy when
              the car is shifted from reverse to
              drive with the brake on may soon
              fail. A transmission that fails to shift
              at the proper speed or shifts rough-
              ly needs adjustment and repair.

☐ Yes **5.** Will the brakes stop the car
☐ No   smoothly?
Brakes that pull a car to one side during panic stops are dangerous and should be repaired.

☐ Yes **6.** Does the car exhaust blue smoke
☐ No   when accelerated rapidly?
Generally a car that exhausts blue smoke has badly worn rings, will use oil and needs expensive engine work.

☐ Yes **7.** Do all the accessories work
☐ No   properly?
The air conditioner, heater, radio, lights, horn, and windshield wipers are expensive to repair.

☐ Yes **8.** Will the engine overheat?
☐ No   A car driven in hot weather, in city traffic with the air conditioner operating, should not cause coolant to boil.

E. Summary of Inspection and Evaluation

_____Yes **1.** Count and compare the number of times you checked yes and the times you checked no.
Write the number of each in the blanks at the left.
_____No

☐ Good **2.** Does your overall rating indicate the car you inspected is in good, fair, or poor
☐ Fair   mechanical condition?
☐ Poor

3. On the basis of your inspection and rating, how much above or below book price should the buyer pay?

$_____ above book price

$_____ book price figure

$_____ below book price

(Continued on next page)

Step 6: Make a decision.

1. If you had the money, would you buy the car you inspected?

_____

2. Why or why not? _____

_____

_____

_____

Step 7: Plan how you will reach your goal.

Once you've made your decision, you need to make a plan. Use the space below to write a paragraph describing what you will do to reach your goal.

_____

_____

_____

_____

_____

_____

_____

_____

_____

_____

_____

_____

_____

_____

_____

_____

CHAPTER 19 Economics and the Consumer

Foundation Skills

*Thinking Skills:
Problem Solving*

Objective: To learn how to handle consumer complaints.

Being a wise consumer means not only buying carefully but also knowing how to handle problems you may have with a company's service or product. Read the following case study of a consumer problem. Then write your answers in the blanks provided.

Tynan saw a newspaper ad for a music CD club. There was no charge to join the club, and new members received five CDs for only $3.99. Club members had to agree to buy four more CDs during the year at the regular club prices.

Tynan carefully printed all the information requested on the membership form and order blank. Then he bought a money order for $3.99. He made a photocopy of the membership form with his money order beside it. He kept that copy and mailed the membership form with the money order to the club's address.

Two weeks later the five CDs arrived, and Tynan liked them very much. Included was a list of other CD titles he could buy at $14.50 each. Tynan checked one CD on the list and bought a money order for $14.50 to pay for that item. He made a photocopy of his order with the money order for his own records. The new CD and a list of more CDs arrived, but Tynan didn't like the new CD very much.

Still, since he had agreed to buy four CDs at the regular club price, he ordered and paid for CDs for three more months. Each time he made a photocopy of his order with his payment.

Tynan had fulfilled his club membership agreement. Because he didn't like most of the CDs, he wrote to the company to cancel his membership. The next month he received a bill for $58.00 for the four CDs he had already paid for.

1. List three things Tynan did that show he was a wise consumer.

   a. _____

   b. _____

   c. _____

2. What should Tynan do first?

   _____

   _____

   _____

(Continued on next page)

3. If the problem is not corrected within a month, what could Tynan do next?

_____

_____

_____

4. Assume you are the person handling customer complaints for the CD club. You have discussed Tynan's purchases and his membership cancellation with your supervisor, who agrees that a mistake has been made and Tynan owes the club no money. Use the space below to write a letter to Tynan. The purpose of your letter is to apologize to Tynan and to create goodwill so that he may once again consider joining the club.

_____

_____

_____

_____

_____

_____

_____

_____

_____

_____

_____

_____

_____

_____

_____

_____

CHAPTER **19** Economics and the Consumer

ACTIVITY 19-4	**Workplace Competencies**
Long-Range Buying Plans	*Resources:* *Allocating Money*

Objective: To identify future needs and make a buying plan.

Some things that you want to buy may be too expensive for you to pay for without first saving some money toward the purchase. Other items may be replacements for things you already have. For example, you may know that in three months you'll need a new winter coat. In these cases, you'll need to make a plan for how you can pay for the items you need. The first step in making your plan is to inventory, or make a list of, the items you already have. When you make your list, note whether the items are in good condition or will need to be replaced soon.

After making the inventory of what you already have, next make a list of items you'll need to buy. This list should include both new items and replacements for things you already have. By using this "Needs" list and planning ahead, you can save money by buying needed items when they go on sale. For this activity, assume that you'll be moving to your own furnished apartment or dormitory when the school year ends. Use the space below to write your long-range buying plan.

Long-Range Buying Plan

Inventory   **Condition**

_____   _____

_____   _____

_____   _____

_____   _____

_____   _____

_____   _____

Items Needed to Buy

_____   _____

_____   _____

_____   _____

CHAPTER *19* Economics and the Consumer

Research

ACTIVITY 19-5
Checking Out Consumer Products

Objective: To gather information that will help you become a wise consumer.

Making a long-range buying plan, as you did in Activity 19-4, is one way to be a wise consumer. Another way to be a wise consumer is to research the major products you buy to learn about the quality of different brands and the special features of each. The highest-priced product is not always the one with the highest quality. Doing a little research can save you money and give you greater satisfaction with your product choices.

Choose one of the items on your long-range buying plan. Conduct research to find out what you should look for in buying this product. For example, if you need to buy clothing, your research might tell you that "tightly woven cloth usually wears longer than open weaves." As you do your research, write the features or product tips in the space provided below.

Consumer magazines, such as *Consumer Reports*, are a good source of information on a variety of products and their manufacturers and prices. If you need help, ask your school or local public librarian to guide you to other sources you can use to find information about the item you want to buy. Try to find out when this product typically goes on sale, and write that information below.

Name of item _____

Month on sale _____

_____

Buying Tips/Product Information

_____

_____

_____

_____

_____

_____

_____

_____

CHAPTER *20* Managing Your Money

ACTIVITY 20-1	**Foundation Skills**
Analyzing a Budget	*Thinking Skills: Problem Solving*

Objective: To analyze and adjust expenses to meet budgeting goals.

When preparing and following a budget, you need to understand your goals and how they affect your budget. For example, if you want to pay off a car loan as soon as possible, you might cut back on entertainment expenses to have more money for the car payments.

For this activity, assume that you prepared the list of income and expenses below. The net earnings amount includes your hope that you'll get a 5 percent raise later this month. You have a goal of saving $2,400 a year so you'll have a cushion for an emergency or, later on, for a down payment on a new car or a home. You also have college loans you're repaying, on which you've been paying $100 a month. This payment is flexible.

Add amounts to find total earnings and total expenses. Then answer the questions.

Income		**Expenses**	
Net earnings	$1,400	Apartment rent	$375
Interest on savings	5	Car payment	250
Total earnings		Insurance (car and rental)	75
		College loans	100
		Food	200
		Clothing	100
		Transportation	90
		Entertainment	60
		Gifts and contributions	40
		Savings	200
		Miscellaneous	10
		Total expenses	

1. Your planned expenses are larger than your total earnings. How would you adjust the budget, keeping in mind the goals given above?

_____

2. Suppose the raise you expected is only 4 percent, which means about $20 less per month in your paycheck. How would you further adjust the budget?

_____

3. Suppose your priority is to pay off your college loans faster, paying for example, $125 a month. How could you adjust your planned expenses to make this larger payment?

_____

CHAPTER *20* Managing Your Money

Foundation Skills

*Basic Skills:
Mathematics*

ACTIVITY 20-2
Planning a Personal Budget

Objective: To examine personal needs and expenses for use in planning a personal budget.

Managing money so that you can pay for the things you need and want requires you to know exactly how you spend your money. For this activity, you will prepare a budget by first listing your goals and then determining your needs. Next, you'll use the expense record provided to list all your expenses for one week. Finally, you'll estimate monthly income and expenses and evaluate your spending habits.

If you have a part-time job, use your take-home earnings in your budget. If you do not have a part-time job, use a take-home earnings amount of $100 a week.

List Your Goals

Make a list of your financial goals on a separate sheet of paper. For example, list the things you want to buy. If you are saving for college or to put money down on a car, list those goals. After making your list, underline or circle the goals that are most important to you. Cross out the things you don't really need.

Record Your Weekly Expenses

Use the expense record below to keep track of what you spend for a week. At the end of the week, total the amount spent for each heading.

Item	Sunday	Monday	Tuesday	Wednesday	Thursday	Friday	Saturday
Food	$	$	$	$	$	$	$
Housing	$	$	$	$	$	$	$
Education	$	$	$	$	$	$	$
Clothing	$	$	$	$	$	$	$
Transportation	$	$	$	$	$	$	$
Medical care	$	$	$	$	$	$	$
Dental	$	$	$	$	$	$	$
Recreation	$	$	$	$	$	$	$
Gifts and contributions	$	$	$	$	$	$	$
Other	$	$	$	$	$	$	$
Total per day	$	$	$	$	$	$	$
Total for week	$						

Estimating a Monthly Budget

Complete the personal budget below. Multiply your weekly total by four to get the monthly estimates for day-to-day expenses. Then answer the questions.

Personal Budget

Total income for month _____

Regular monthly expenses:

    Rent or mortgage payment _____

    Utilities _____

    Household maintenance and repairs _____

    Installment payments _____

    Savings _____

    Other _____

    Total _____

Day-to-Day Expenses

    Food _____

    Housing _____

    Education _____

    Clothing _____

    Transportation _____

    Medical/dental care _____

    Recreation _____

    Gifts and contributions _____

    Total _____

Total monthly expenses _____

---

1. Compare your income with your savings and expenses for the month.

   Total savings and expenses _____

   Total income _____

2. Are you staying within budget? If not, how will you revise your budget?

   _____

   _____

CHAPTER *20* Managing Your Money

ACTIVITY 20-3	**Foundation Skills**

Preparing a Future Budget

Thinking Skills:
Decision Making

Objective: To practice planning a budget for your future lifestyle.

In just a few years you will be taking on more financial responsibility. You'll probably support yourself. You may even set aside some money to help you achieve your future lifestyle goals. For this activity, you are to apply what you have learned about managing your money to planning a one-year budget for yourself.

Assume you will start work next week on your first job. You will receive monthly take-home pay of $1,295. Federal and state income taxes and Social Security are withheld. Also, medical/hospital insurance will already be deducted. You are single and live in a furnished apartment but pay all utility charges. Check the classified section of your local newspaper for rental rates. Monthly car payments, including car insurance, are $375.

Use the budget plan on the next page to list your expenses. Refer to the buying plan you prepared for Activity 19-4, and use these expenses in your budget. Think of other expenses that might increase by having a full-time job, such as additional expenses for commuting and for dry-cleaning bills.

List each expense under one of the three headings and plan a balanced budget for one year. If you wish, use the space below to do any necessary figuring. Compare your budget with those of your classmates.

Planning and calculation space:

Budget Plan		
Fixed Expenses	**One Month**	**One Year**
Total		
Flexible Expenses	**One Month**	**One Year**
Total		
Day-to-Day Expenses	**One Month**	**One Year**
Total		
	One Month	**One Year**
Income	_____	_____
Less fixed expenses	_____	_____
Balance	_____	_____
Less flexible expenses	_____	_____
Balance	_____	_____
Less day-to-day expenses	_____	_____
Potential additional savings		

CHAPTER 20 Managing Your Money

ACTIVITY 20-4	**Workplace Competencies**
Examining a Family Budget	*Resources:* *Allocating Money*

Objective: To study a family budget and learn financial responsibility.

As an adult, you may have the responsibility of managing family income to meet the important needs and wants of family members. Making a budget and sticking to it is one of the best ways to manage money responsibly.

One way to learn budgeting is to study a typical family's spending plan. A copy of the Chan family's budget for one year is shown below and on the next page. The budget is based on last year's expenses and this year's expected income. Study this budget carefully and answer the questions listed on the next page.

The Chans' budget uses a standard method. Expenses are listed under three headings—fixed expenses, flexible expenses, and day-to-day expenses. Fixed expenses must be paid on certain dates during the year. They include taxes, rent or house payments, insurance, professional and union dues, and other such expenses. Flexible expenses may be adjusted to meet unexpected changes in spending. Many items under this heading change during the year. They include clothing, recreation, newspapers and magazines, medical care, and emergency (unplanned) expenses.

Day-to-day expenses make up a sizable part of the family's expenses, but they, too, are flexible expenses. Budgeting in this area helps control spending.

Fixed Expenses	**One Month**	**One Year**
1. Taxes (not withheld)		
Federal income	$ 80.00	$ 960.00
State income	20.00	240.00
Property	70.00	840.00
2. House payments	500.00	6,000.00
3. Car payments	150.00	1,800.00
4. Furniture payments	50.00	600.00
5. Safe-deposit box rent	1.00	12.00
6. Insurance premiums		
Medical/hospital	75.00	900.00
Car	55.00	660.00
Life	80.00	960.00
Homeowner's	40.00	480.00
7. Professional dues	20.00	240.00
8. Savings	200.00	2,400.00
Subtotal	$ 1,341.00	$ 16,092.00

Flexible Expenses	One Month	One Year
1. Clothing	$ 100.00	$ 1,200.00
2. Contributions & gifts		
Church	30.00	360.00
Charities	10.00	120.00
Civic groups	5.00	60.00
Gifts (birthday, wedding, etc.)	10.00	120.00
3. Newspapers & magazines	20.00	240.00
4. Medical & dental care	50.00	600.00
5. Recreation & vacation	50.00	600.00
6. Emergencies	50.00	600.00
Subtotal	$ 325.00	$ 3,900.00

Day-to-Day Living Costs	One Month	One Year
1. Food	$ 400.00	$ 4,800.00
2. Laundry & dry-cleaning	50.00	600.00
3. Personal care (haircuts, cosmetics, soap, etc.)	50.00	600.00
4. Household operation		
Fuel	75.00	900.00
Electricity	60.00	720.00
Telephone	40.00	480.00
Water	20.00	240.00
Maintenance	25.00	300.00
5. Automobile		
Gas & oil	150.00	1,800.00
Repair & maintenance	30.00	360.00
6. Bus fares	60.00	720.00
7. Pocket money		
Lucy Chan	40.00	480.00
Thom Chan	40.00	480.00
Bill Chan	20.00	240.00
Amy Chan	20.00	240.00
8. School (books, activities, etc.)	25.00	300.00
9. Miscellaneous	50.00	600.00
Subtotal	$ 1,155.00	$ 13,860.00

Income	One Month	One Year
Wages (after withholding tax deductions)	$ 2,772.00	$ 33,264.00
Other income (interest, dividends)	49.00	588.00
Total Income	$ 2,821.00	$ 33,852.00
Total Expenses (including savings)	$ 2,821.00	$ 33,852.00

1. Which expense in the Chans' budget is the largest? _____

2. What part of the budget could be used if the Chans plan to take a vacation costing $2,000.00?

_____

3. Suppose the Chans wanted to save an additional $800.00 each year for Bill's and Amy's education. Where should they try to lower expenses?

_____

CHAPTER 20 Managing Your Money

ACTIVITY 20-5	Research
Budgeting with Software	

Objective: To learn about software programs that can be used to create and monitor budgets.

Several software programs are available that allow you to prepare a budget and to keep your financial records. Two examples of such programs are Quicken (made by the Intuit Company) and Microsoft Money (made by Microsoft Corporation).

For this activity, you are to research a financial software program of your choice. If you do not have access to such a program (either at school, at your public library, or at home), use computer magazines to read articles evaluating and comparing the features of different money-management programs. Magazines such as *PC World, PC Magazine, Macworld,* and *Byte* all publish regular articles about software programs and have onine editions. Microsoft and Intuit also maintain Web sites with information about their products.

Use your research to answer the following questions.

1. What is the name of the software you chose? _____

2. What is the cost of this software? _____

3. List the types of financial activities you can do with this program.

   _____

   _____

   _____

4. What are some special features of this program?

   _____

   _____

   _____

5. How would using the program you researched help you with a personal budget?

   _____

   _____

   _____

CHAPTER *21* Banking and Credit

ACTIVITY 21-1

Investing Your Money

Foundation Skills

Basic Skills:
Mathematics

Objective: To graph an investment's growth in value over a period of ten years.

Salya Roberts has savings of $1,000, and she wants to invest it for ten years. Salya has her savings in a passbook account paying 3.5 percent interest. If she invests her money in a CD (certificate of deposit), she can earn 5 percent. If she chooses a money market account, she can earn 6 percent. Both are compounded annually. Calculate the growth in $1,000 at each interest rate (5 percent and 6 percent) for a period of ten years. Use a dotted line to show the 5 percent investment and a solid line for the 6 percent investment.

Growth of $1,000 Invested for Ten Years

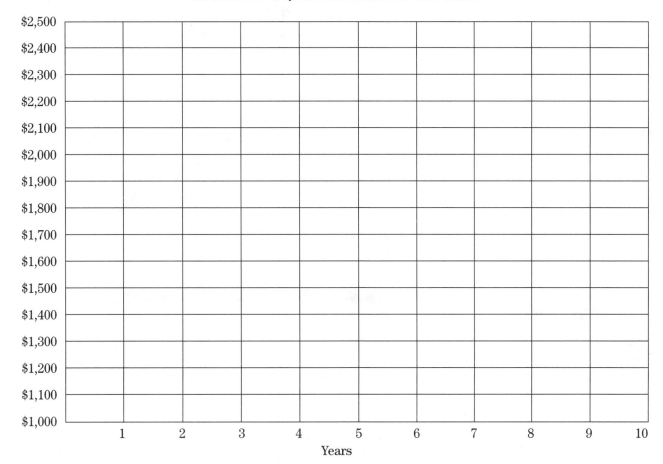

Years

1. How much will Salya's investment be worth at 5 percent interest in ten years? _____

2. How much will the investment be worth at 6 percent in ten years? _____

Name ____________________ Date ____________________

Class ____________________ Instructor ____________________

CHAPTER 21 Banking and Credit

ACTIVITY 21-2

Writing Checks

Foundation Skills

Basic Skills: Writing

Objective: To learn how to write checks and record them properly in a check register.

Imagine that you are buying a pair of inline skates for $115.35 from the Harmon Sports Mart. You want to pay for your purchase by writing a check. This is the first check to be entered in your new check register. Your balance in the check register is $378.97. Complete the check register, then write the check to pay for your skates. Use the current date.

RECORD ALL CHARGES THAT AFFECT YOUR BANK ACCOUNT

NUMBER	DATE	DESCRIPTION OF TRANSACTION	PAYMENT/DEBIT (−)	✓ T	FEE (IF ANY) (−)	DEPOSIT/CREDIT (+)	BALANCE $

BANK IV

BANK IV Pittsburg, N.A.
Pittsburg, Kansas

83-24
1011

Date ____________________ No. 405

Pay to the Order of ____________________ $ __________

____________________ Dollars

For ____________________ Signature ____________________

⑆101100249 4018 4926 405⑈

CHAPTER 21   Banking and Credit

ACTIVITY 21-3	**Foundation Skills**
Balancing Your Checkbook	*Basic Skills: Arithmetic*

Objective: To practice balancing a checkbook using a bank statement, canceled checks, and deposit slips.

    Talitha Smith received her November bank statement and canceled checks on December 5. Two checks she had written were not returned with the bank statement: Check 216, for $100, and Check 217, for $75. Talitha also made a deposit on November 30 of $125, which is not shown on the bank statement.

    Use the form shown below to balance Talitha's checking account. Talitha's bank statement is shown on the next page.

Five Steps to Balance Your Account

Outstanding Checks, Withdrawals, Transfers

1. Enter the ending balance shown on this statement. _____

Transaction	Amount

2. Enter deposits not shown on this statement. + _____
_____
_____
_____
_____
_____

3. Total steps one and two. _____

Total	$

4. Enter the total (from right) of outstanding checks, ATM withdrawals, and electronic transfers not shown on this statement. − _____

5. Subtract step four from step three. After deducting the service charge from the checkbook balance, this number should match your checkbook balance. _____

(Continued on next page)

```
BANK IV    BANK IV Pittsburg, N.A.
           E.F.T. Department                    ACCOUNT STATEMENT
           Pittsburg, KS 66762-0599
```

TALITHA SMITH
220 LAKEVIEW DRIVE
PITTSBURG, KS 66781-0524

Statement Date – 12/05/0X 1	Page Number 1

Account Summary:

Beginning balance	1,145.50
4 deposits	800.00
6 checks	600.00
2 ATM withdrawals	120.00
Service charge	5.00
Ending balance	1,220.50

DATE	TRANSACTION	AMOUNT	BALANCE
11/01	Deposit	200.00	1,345.50
11/02	Check 210	250.00	1,095.50
11/02	Check 211	50.00	1,045.50
11/02	Check 212	50.00	995.50
11/04	ATM withdrawal	50.00	945.50
11/08	Deposit	200.00	1,145.50
11/15	Check 213	100.00	1,045.50
11/15	Deposit	200.00	1,245.50
11/20	Check 214	100.00	1,145.50
11/21	ATM withdrawal	70.00	1,075.50
11/22	Deposit	200.00	1,275.50
11/25	Check 215	50.00	1,225.50
11/30	Service charge	5.00	1,220.50

1. Where is the service charge recorded? _____

2. What balance should appear on Talitha's check register after the bank statement is reconciled?

_____

3. What will be the beginning balance of next month's bank statement?

_____

CHAPTER *21* Banking and Credit

ACTIVITY 21-4	Workplace Competencies
Evaluating Credit Card Contracts	*Information: Acquiring and Evaluating Information*

Objective: To compare credit costs among creditors.

Credit card companies use different methods to calculate the balance upon which they assess finance charges. Some creditors add finance charges after subtracting payments made during the billing period. This practice is called the adjusted balance method. Other creditors calculate interest without considering payments made. This practice is called the previous balance method. Using a third method, creditors add your balance for each day of the billing period and then divide by the number of days in that period. The result is the average daily balance, on which interest is charged.

Study the example of the three billing methods below. Then answer the questions that follow.

Billing Method	Monthly Interest Rate	Previous Balance	Payments	Interest Charge
Adjusted Balance	1.5%	$400.00	$300.00	$1.50 ($100 × 1.5%)
Previous Balance	1.5%	$400.00	$300.00	$6.00 ($400 × 1.5%)
Average Daily Balance	1.5%	$400.00	$300.00	$3.75 (average balance of $250 × 1.5%)

1. Which would be the least expensive method of calculating interest if you paid the bill in full each month?

_____

2. Which method would be least expensive if you pay only a part of the bill each month?

_____

3. Obtain contracts for three different credit cards (VISA, MasterCard, Discover Card, American Express, or others) and check each contract for type of billing method used. List the credit card and its billing methods in the space below.

Credit Card   **Billing Method**

_____   _____

_____   _____

_____   _____

CHAPTER 21 Banking and Credit

ACTIVITY 21-5
Doing a Credit Survey

Objective: To compare credit costs among creditors.

For this activity, you are to compare interest rates charged by different types of creditors in your community. Your teacher will assign you to a committee. Each committee is to request the cost for a personal loan of $2,000 for one year from one bank, one credit union, and one online loan service. Write the information you obtain in the spaces below. Then present your findings to the class in a short, oral report.

Name of bank _____

Interest rate _____   Co-signer needed? Yes _____   No _____

Additional charges _____

Name of credit union _____

Interest rate _____   Co-signer needed? Yes _____   No _____

Additional charges _____

Name and URL of online loan service _____

Interest rate _____   Co-signer needed? Yes _____   No _____

Additional charges _____

Questions

1. Which institution offers the best credit rate? _____

2. How many of the institutions would require a co-signer for your loan?

_____

3. Did any institution require additional charges? If so, for what?

_____

CHAPTER 22   Buying Insurance

ACTIVITY 22-1	Foundation Skills
Comparing Auto Insurance Rates	*Thinking Skills: Knowing How to Learn*

Objective: To learn about different kinds of coverages and rates for auto insurance.

Your teacher will form your class into three committees. Each committee is to find out about the rates charged by one well-known company that insures autos in your area. Each committee may visit, telephone, or write the company it selects.

Request the rates for a 2000 Honda Accord being driven an estimated mileage of over 7,500 miles per year. Assume the car is driven less than 30 miles a day to work or school. From each company, obtain the cost of the types of insurance coverage listed in the chart below. To compare the total cost of insurance quoted by the three companies, each committee is to present its information to the class, including visuals that highlight costs for the categories listed in the chart. Then answer the questions on the next page.

Coverage	Driver Male, 20 Years Old		Driver Female, 20 Years Old	
	Single	Married	Single	Married
Liability				
Bodily injury				
$100,000 each person				
$300,000 each accident				
Property damage				
$15,000 each accident				
Uninsured motorists				
Bodily injury				
$100,000 each person				
$300,000 each accident				
Comprehensive				
Collision—$250 deductible				
Emergency road service				
SUBTOTAL				
Discounts				
Airbags/passive restraints				
Good-student discount				
Drug/alcohol education				
Antitheft devices				
Multi-car discount				
Driver training discount				
TOTAL AFTER DISCOUNTS				

(Continued on next page)

1. Do the rates of the three companies differ for male and female drivers? If so, explain why.

   _____

   _____

   _____

2. How do companies' rates compare for single and married persons?

   _____

   _____

3. Do all of the companies give discounts for good-student ratings?

   _____

   _____

4. Do any of the companies offer discounts not listed in the table? If so, what?

   _____

   _____

   _____

5. Which company charges the least for the same insurance coverage?

   _____

   _____

6. Which company charges the most for the same insurance coverage?

   _____

   _____

7. What reasons might explain the differences in cost for the same insurance coverage?

   _____

   _____

   _____

   _____

   _____

   _____

CHAPTER 22 Buying Insurance

ACTIVITY 22-2	Foundation Skills

ACTIVITY 22-2

*Comparing Life
Insurance Policies*

Foundation Skills

*Thinking Skills:
Knowing How to Learn*

Objective: To compare life insurance rates.

    With your teacher, form three committees to study life insurance rates. Each committee is to select a local insurance company and visit, telephone, or write the company to obtain information.

    Since each company will probably offer a number of different options, restrict your survey to the following: (1) a 20-year term insurance for $100,000, and (b) a whole life insurance policy for $100,000.

    Two people (not a couple) are to be insured: a 22-year-old male and a 22-year-old female, both in good health who neither smoke nor use drugs. Share your findings with the class and record the rates in the chart below. Discuss the findings, then answer the questions that follow.

Type of Policy	Company A		Company B		Company C	
	Male	**Female**	**Male**	**Female**	**Male**	**Female**
20-Year Term Insurance						
Total premiums, 20 years						
Cash value at 20 years						
Whole Life Insurance						
Total premiums, 20 years						
Cash value at 20 years						

1. Is there any difference between companies in the premiums? If yes, why?

_____

_____

2. Are premiums for males and females different? Why?

_____

_____

3. Which company would you select for your purchase of life insurance? Why?

_____

_____

CHAPTER 22 Buying Insurance

ACTIVITY 22-3	**Workplace Competencies**
Making a Personal Property Inventory	*Technology: Selecting Technology and Applying Technology to Task*

Objective: To use a computer to itemize your personal property for insurance coverage.

Whether you live in an apartment or a home, you should probably have personal property insurance to cover potential losses from theft, fire, smoke, or water. If your property is stolen or damaged, you'll need to provide your insurance company with a record of the property, including an estimate of the cost of each item. The best way to be prepared is to keep an inventory of personal property.

Using the form on the next page as a guide, set up a personal inventory record using a computer program. This form can be set up using either spreadsheet or word processing software. Choose a program, then complete the activity by listing your own personal property.

If you do not have access to a computer, complete the form on the next page. Then answer the questions below.

1. What is your estimate of the total purchase cost of your personal property?

_____

2. Do you think you need personal property insurance? Explain why or why not.

_____

_____

_____

_____

3. Since your personal property record could be lost or damaged in a fire, what could you do to protect it while still having access to update it with new purchases?

_____

_____

_____

_____

Personal Property Inventory

Electronic items:	Purchase Price	Date of Purchase	Tools (Cont'd.)	Purchase Price	Date of Purchase
Television					
CD player					
Radio					
Stereo			Collections:		
Camera					
Computer/printer					
Other:					
Jewelry:			Other valubles:		
Watch					
Rings					
Other:					
			Furniture:		
Sports equipment:					
Musical instruments:			Silverware, dishes, glassware:		
Clothing:					
Coats					
Suits					
Dresses					
Blouses					
Shirts			Electrical appliances:		
Pants/skirts					
Lingerie/underwear					
Shoes/boots					
Other:					
			Linens:		
Tools:					

CHAPTER 22 Buying Insurance

ACTIVITY 22-4

Research

Comparing Costs for Renter's Insurance

Objective: To learn about the cost of buying renter's insurance for personal property.

Chances are you'll live in an apartment at some time in the future. When you do, you'll need to consider buying personal property insurance. For this activity, you are to obtain information on the terms and costs of renter's insurance offered by three companies in your area.

You may choose to telephone an agent or write a letter. When requesting information, ask for coverage of $20,000 for a single, 19-year-old person living in an apartment. Ask for rates for two different types of apartments: one in an apartment complex with ten or more apartments, the other in a single-family home with an apartment added to the building. Both are of brick construction.

Use the table below to record your findings. Then answer the questions below.

Type of Dwelling	Annual Premium		
	Company A	Company B	Company C
Single-family home with attached second-floor apartment			
Ten (or more) unit building, first-floor apartment			

1. Is there a difference in the premiums for the two types of buildings? If so, explain why.

_____

_____

_____

2. If there a difference between first- and second-floor apartments? Why or why not?

_____

_____

_____

3. Which company offers you the best price for the coverage needed?

_____

CHAPTER *23* Taxes and Social Security

ACTIVITY 23-1	**Foundation Skills**

*Figuring Your
Withholding Allowance*

*Basic Skills:
Mathematics*

Objective: To practice figuring withholding allowance and filling out a W-4 form.

When you begin your first job, your employer will ask you to fill out Form W-4, Employee's Withholding Allowance Certificate. The information you write on this form will tell the employer how much money to withhold from your pay for federal income tax.

Each allowance you claim lowers the amount of tax that the employer must withhold from your pay. You may claim an allowance for yourself, an allowance for each dependent, and certain other credits (see lines E through G on the Personal Allowance Worksheet on the next page).

Using the information below, complete the Personal Allowance Worksheet and fill out the W-4 form on the next page. Compare your answers with those of your classmates. Then answer the questions below.

> Mary E. Léon is single. No one claims her as a dependent, and she has no dependents. Mary works at one job and expects to earn a bit over $20,000 this year. Last year she earned a little less. Mary's Social Security number is 990-00-4321. Her address is 1920 May Street, Pittsburg, KS 66762. She shares her apartment with two roommates.

1. In the paragraph above, what information is pertinent to filling out the Personal Allowance Worksheet?

   _____

   _____

   _____

   _____

2. What information is not pertinent to completing this form?

   _____

   _____

   _____

   _____

(Continued on next page)

Personal Allowances Worksheet

A   Enter "1" for **yourself** if no one else can claim you as a dependent . . . . **A** _____

B   Enter "1" if: {   • You are single and have only one job; or
       • You are married, have only one job, and your spouse does not work; or   } . . **B** _____
       • Your wages from a second job or your spouse's wages (or the total of both) are $1,000 or less.

C   Enter "1" for your **spouse**. But, you may choose to enter -0- if you are married and have either a working spouse or more than one job (this may help you avoid having too little tax withheld) . . . . **C** _____

D   Enter number of **dependents** (other than your spouse or yourself) whom you will claim on your tax return . . . . . **D** _____

E   Enter "1" if you will file as **head of household** on your tax return (see conditions under **Head of Household** above) . **E** _____

F   Enter "1" if you have at least $1,500 of **child or dependent care expenses** for which you plan to claim a credit . . **F** _____

G   Add lines A through F and enter total here. **Note:** This amount may be different from the number of exemptions you claim on your return ▶ **G** _____

For accuracy, do all worksheets that apply. {   • If you plan to **itemize or claim adjustments to income** and want to reduce your withholding, see the Deductions and Adjustments Worksheet on page 2.

    • If you are **single** and have **more than one job** and your combined earnings from all jobs exceed $30,000 OR if you are **married** and have a **working spouse or more than one job,** and the combined earnings from all jobs exceed $50,000, see the Two-Earner/Two-Job Worksheet on page 2 if you want to avoid having too little tax withheld.

    • If **neither** of the above situations applies, **stop here** and enter the number from line G on line 5 of Form W-4 below.

- - - - - - - - - - - - **Cut here and give the certificate to your employer. Keep the top portion for your records.** - - - - - - - - - - - -

Form **W-4**
Department of the Treasury
Internal Revenue Service

Employee's Withholding Allowance Certificate

OMB No. 1545-0010

▶ **For Privacy Act and Paperwork Reduction Act Notice, see reverse.**

1 Type or print your first name and middle initial Last name	**2** Your social security number	

Home address (number and street or rural route)	**3** ☐ Single ☐ Married ☐ Married, but withhold at higher Single rate. **Note:** If married, but legally separated, or spouse is a nonresident alien, check the Single box.
City or town, state, and ZIP code	**4** If your last name differs from that on your social security card, check here and call 1-800-772-1213 for more information . . . . ▶ ☐

5   Total number of allowances you are claiming (from line G above or from the worksheets on page 2 if they apply) .   **5** _____

6   Additional amount, if any, you want withheld from each paycheck . . . .   **6** $ _____

7   I claim exemption from withholding for 199X and I certify that I meet **BOTH** of the following conditions for exemption:
- Last year I had a right to a refund of **ALL** Federal income tax withheld because I had **NO** tax liability; **AND**
- This year I expect a refund of **ALL** Federal income tax withheld because I expect to have **NO** tax liability.

If you meet both conditions, enter "EXEMPT" here . . . . ▶ **7** _____

Under penalties of perjury, I certify that I am entitled to the number of withholding allowances claimed on this certificate or entitled to claim exempt status.

Employee's signature ▶ _____   Date ▶ _____ 20 _____

8 Employer's name and address (Employer: Complete 8 and 10 only if sending to the IRS)	**9** Office code (optional)	**10** Employer identification number

Cat. No. 10220Q

CHAPTER **23** Taxes and Social Security

ACTIVITY 23-2	**Foundation Skills**
The W-2 Wage and Tax Statement	*Thinking Skills: Reasoning*

Objective: To analyze the types of information reported on the W-2 form.

As you read in your textbook chapter, a W-2 form is a statement of how much money you earned and the amount of taxes that were withheld for the preceding year. You must have this form to prepare your tax return.

Read the information below and study the W-2 form that follows. Then answer the questions on the next page.

Terry Reed, a high school student, worked for Taylor Office Supply during the summer. In September he returned to school as a full-time student but continued to work on weekends. In January of the next year, Terry received three copies of the W-2 form from Taylor Office Supply.

a Control number			OMB No. 1545-0008		
b Employer's identification number 10-22674340			1 Wages, tips, other compensation $2,850.00	2 Federal income tax withheld $427.50	
c Employer's name, address, and ZIP code Taylor Office Supply 900 River Road Pittsburg, KS 66762			3 Social security wages $2,850.00	4 Social security tax withheld $218.03	
			5 Medicare wages and tips	6 Medicare tax withheld	
			7 Social security tips	8 Allocated tips	
d Employee's social security number 999-00-1010			9 Advance EIC payment	10 Dependent care benefits	
e Employee's name, address, and ZIP code Terry Reed 2520 East Elm Avenue Pittsburg, KS 66762			11 Nonqualified plans	12 Benefits included in box 1	
			13 See Instrs. for box 13	14 Other	
			15 Statutory employee ☐ Deceased ☐ Pension plan ☐ Legal rep. ☐ Hshld. emp. ☐ Subtotal ☐ Deferred compensation ☐		
16 State Employer's state I.D. No.	17 State wages, tips, etc.	18 State income tax	19 Locality name	20 Local wages, tips, etc.	21 Local income tax

(1)   Department of the Treasury—Internal Revenue Service

Form **W-2** **Wage and Tax Statement**
Copy B To Be Filed With Employee's FEDERAL Tax Return

This information is being furnished to the Internal Revenue Service.

5 WA

(Continued on next page)

1. How much money was withheld for federal income tax on Terry's W-2 form?

_____

2. How much money was withheld for Social Security?

_____

3. How much money did Terry earn working for Taylor Office Supply?

_____

4. Which copy of the W-2 form will Terry attach to his federal tax return?

_____

5. Did Taylor Office Supply withhold any money from Terry's paycheck for state and local taxes?

_____

CHAPTER *23* Taxes and Social Security

ACTIVITY 23-3	Foundation Skills
Filing a 1040EZ Income Tax Return	*Personal Qualities: Responsibility*

Objective: To practice filling out a federal tax return.

For this activity, you are to complete the 1040EZ form on the next page for Louisa B. Tallman. Louisa works full-time for the Gray Sports Marketing Agency. She is not claimed as a dependent on another person's return and wants to give $3 to the Presidential Election Campaign Fund. Use the W-2 Wage and Tax Statement and 1099 Interest Income Statement that appear on page 245 to help you fill out the tax return. A part of the tax table for taxpayers with taxable income of $9,000 to $21,000 appears on page 246 for your use in filing Louisa's tax return.

Once you have completed the return, use the checklist below to check your work.

How to Avoid Common Mistakes	Mistakes may delay your refund or result in notices being sent to you.
	1. Check your math, especially when figuring your taxable income, Federal income tax withheld, and your refund or amount you owe.
	2. Remember to sign and date Form 1040EZ and enter your occupation.
	3. Use the amount from line 6 to find your tax in the tax table. Be sure you enter the correct tax on line 10.
	4. Check the "Yes" box on line 5 if you (or your spouse) can be claimed as a dependent on someone's return, such as your parent's return. Check "Yes" even if that person chooses not to claim you (or your spouse). If no one can claim you (or your spouse) as a dependent, check the "No" box.
	5. Be sure to enter an amount on line 5. If you check the "Yes" box on line 5, fill in the worksheet on the back of Form 1040EZ to figure the amount to enter. If you check the "No" box, enter 6,550.00 if single; 11,800.00 if married filing jointly.
	6. If you got a peel-off label, make sure it shows the correct name(s), address, and social security number(s). If not, enter the correct information.
	7. If you did not get a peel-off label, enter your name, address, and social security number (SSN) in the spaces provided on Form 1040EZ. If you are married filing jointly, enter your spouse's name and SSN.
	8. Attach your W-2 form(s) to the left margin of your return.
Filing Your Return	Mail your return by April 15, 200X. Use the envelope that came with your booklet. If you don't have that envelope, see the 1040EZ booklet for the address to use.
	You may also file electronically using a personal computer, a modem, and IRS-accepted tax software. Electronic filing is also available through many paid tax return preparers when they prepare your return for you. The IRS's free Volunteer Income Tax Assistance (VITA) and Tax Counseling for the Elderly (TCE) programs may also be able to help you file your return electronically. See the 1040EZ booklet for details on these programs.

(Continued on next page)

Name _____ Date _____

Class _____ Instructor _____

Department of the Treasury—Internal Revenue Service
Income Tax Return for Single and Joint Filers With No Dependents (L)

OMB No. 1545-0675

Use the IRS label here	Your first name and initial — Last name
	If a joint return, spouse's first name and initial — Last name
	Home address (number and street). If you have a P.O. box, see page 7. — Apt. no.
	City, town, or post office, state, and ZIP code. If you have a foreign address, see page 7.

Your social security number

Spouse's social security number

Presidential Election Campaign (See page 7.)

Note: *Checking "Yes" will not change your tax or reduce your refund.*
Do you want $3 to go to this fund? ▶ Yes ☐ No ☐

If a joint return, does your spouse want $3 to go to this fund? ▶ Yes ☐ No ☐

Dollars   Cents

Income

Attach Copy B of Form(s) W-2 here. Enclose, but do not attach any payment with your return.

1 Total wages, salaries, and tips. This should be shown in box 1 of your W-2 form(s). Attach your W-2 form(s). 1

2 Taxable interest income of $400 or less. If the total is over $400, you cannot use Form 1040EZ. 2

3 Unemployment compensation (see page 9). 3

4 Add lines, 1, 2, and 3. This is your **adjusted gross income.** If under $9,500, see page 9 to find out if you can claim the earned income credit on line 8. 4

Note: *You must check Yes or No.*

5 Can your parents (or someone else) claim you on their return?
Yes. Enter amount from worksheet on back. ☐
No. If **single**, enter 6,550.00. If **married**, enter 11,800.00. See back for explanation. ☐ 5

6 Subtract line 5 from line 4. If line 5 is larger than line 4, enter 0. This is your **taxable income.** ▶ 6

Payments and tax

7 Enter your Federal income tax withheld from box 2 of your W-2 form(s). 7

8 **Earned income credit** (see page 9). Enter type and amount of nontaxable earned income below.
Type _____ $ _____ 8

9 Add lines 7 and 8 (do not include nontaxable earned income). These are your **total payments.** 9

10 **Tax.** Use the amount on **line 6** to find your tax in the tax table on pages 20–24 of the booklet. Then, enter the tax from the table on this line. 10

Refund

Have it sent directly to your bank account! See page 13 and fill in 11b, c, and d.

11a If line 9 is larger than line 10, subtract line 10 from line 9. This is your **refund.** 11a

b Routing number

c Type Checking ☐ Savings ☐

d Account number

Amount you owe

12 If line 10 is larger than line 9, subtract line 9 from line 10. This is the **amount you owe.** See page 13 for details on how to pay and what to write on your payment. 12

For Official Use Only

Sign here

Keep copy for your records.

I have read this return. Under penalties of perjury, I declare that to the best of my knowledge and belief, the return is true, correct, and accurately lists all amounts and sources of income I received during the tax year.

Your signature	Spouse's signature if joint return
Date — Your occupation	Date — Spouse's occupation

PAYER'S name, street address, city, state, and ZIP code

Pittsburg Credit Union
900 North 4th Street
Pittsburg, KS 66762

☐ CORRECTED

OMB No. 1545-0112

Statement for Recipients of

Interest Income

PAYER'S Federal identification number	RECIPIENT'S identification number
40-7654321	999-00-1234

1 Earnings from savings and loan associations, credit unions, bank deposits, bearer certificates of deposit, etc.

$75.00

RECIPIENT'S name, street address, city, state, and ZIP code

Louisa B. Tallman
4400 South Main St.
Pittsburg, KS 66762

2 Early withdrawal penalty

3 U.S. Savings Bonds, etc.

4 Federal income tax withheld

5 Foreign tax paid, (if eligible for foreign tax credit)

6 Foreign country or U.S. possession

**Copy B
For Recipient**

This is important tax information and is being furnished to the Internal Revenue Service. If you are required to file a return, a negligence penalty or other sanction will be imposed on you if this income is taxable and the IRS determines that it has not been reported.

ER-56 8-89

Form **1099-INT**

Department of the Treasury - Internal Revenue Service

---

a Control number		OMB No. 1545-0008	This information is being furnished to the Internal Revenue Service. If you are required to file a tax return, a negligence penalty or other sanction may be imposed on you if this income is taxable and you fail to report it.	

b Employer's identification number	**1** Wages, tips, other compensation	**2** Federal income tax withheld
0-9904300	$15,888.00	$1,509.36

c Employer's name, address, and ZIP code	**3** Social security wages	**4** Social security tax withheld
Gray Sports Marketing Agency 950 River Road Pittsburg, KS 66762	$15,888.00	$1,215.43
	5 Medicare wages and tips	**6** Medicare tax withheld
	7 Social security tips	**8** Allocated tips

d Employee's social security number	**9** Advance EIC payment	**10** Dependent care benefits
999-00-1234		

e Employee's name, address, and ZIP code	**11** Nonqualified plans	**12** Benefits included in box 1
Louisa B. Tallman 4400 South Main St. Pittsburg, KS 66762	**13** See Instrs. for box 13	**14** Other

15 ☐ Statutory employee ☐ Deceased ☐ Pension plan ☐ Legal rep. ☐ Hshld. emp. ☐ Subtotal ☐ Deferred compensation

16 State	Employer's state I.D. No.	**17** State wages, tips, etc.	**18** State income tax	**19** Locality name	**20** Local wages, tips, etc.	**21** Local income tax

(1)

Department of the Treasury—Internal Revenue Service

Form **W-2** **Wage and Tax Statement**

Copy C for EMPLOYEE'S RECORDS (See Notice on back.)

5 WA

(Continued on next page)

1040EZ Tax Table—*Continued*

If Form 1040EZ, line 6, is— At least	But less than	Single	Married filing jointly
9,000			
9,000	9,050	1,354	1,354
9,050	9,100	1,361	1,361
9,100	9,150	1,369	1,369
9,150	9,200	1,376	1,376
9,200	9,250	1,384	1,384
9,250	9,300	1,391	1,391
9,300	9,350	1,399	1,399
9,350	9,400	1,406	1,406
9,400	9,450	1,414	1,414
9,450	9,500	1,421	1,421
9,500	9,550	1,429	1,429
9,550	9,600	1,436	1,436
9,600	9,650	1,444	1,444
9,650	9,700	1,451	1,451
9,700	9,750	1,459	1,459
9,750	9,800	1,466	1,466
9,800	9,850	1,474	1,474
9,850	9,900	1,481	1,481
9,900	9,950	1,489	1,489
9,950	10,000	1,496	1,496
10,000			
10,000	10,050	1,504	1,504
10,050	10,100	1,511	1,511
10,100	10,150	1,519	1,519
10,150	10,200	1,526	1,526
10,200	10,250	1,534	1,534
10,250	10,300	1,541	1,541
10,300	10,350	1,549	1,549
10,350	10,400	1,556	1,556
10,400	10,450	1,564	1,564
10,450	10,500	1,571	1,571
10,500	10,550	1,579	1,579
10,550	10,600	1,586	1,586
10,600	10,650	1,594	1,594
10,650	10,700	1,601	1,601
10,700	10,750	1,609	1,609
10,750	10,800	1,616	1,616
10,800	10,850	1,624	1,624
10,850	10,900	1,631	1,631
10,900	10,950	1,639	1,639
10,950	11,000	1,646	1,646
11,000			
11,000	11,050	1,654	1,654
11,050	11,100	1,661	1,661
11,100	11,150	1,669	1,669
11,150	11,200	1,676	1,676
11,200	11,250	1,684	1,684
11,250	11,300	1,691	1,691
11,300	11,350	1,699	1,699
11,350	11,400	1,706	1,706
11,400	11,450	1,714	1,714
11,450	11,500	1,721	1,721
11,500	11,550	1,729	1,729
11,550	11,600	1,736	1,736
11,600	11,650	1,744	1,744
11,650	11,700	1,751	1,751
11,700	11,750	1,759	1,759
11,750	11,800	1,766	1,766
11,800	11,850	1,774	1,774
11,850	11,900	1,781	1,781
11,900	11,950	1,789	1,789
11,950	12,000	1,796	1,796

If Form 1040EZ, line 6, is— At least	But less than	Single	Married filing jointly
12,000			
12,000	12,050	1,804	1,804
12,050	12,100	1,811	1,811
12,100	12,150	1,819	1,819
12,150	12,200	1,826	1,826
12,200	12,250	1,834	1,834
12,250	12,300	1,841	1,841
12,300	12,350	1,849	1,849
12,350	12,400	1,856	1,856
12,400	12,450	1,864	1,864
12,450	12,500	1,871	1,871
12,500	12,550	1,879	1,879
12,550	12,600	1,886	1,886
12,600	12,650	1,894	1,894
12,650	12,700	1,901	1,901
12,700	12,750	1,909	1,909
12,750	12,800	1,916	1,916
12,800	12,850	1,924	1,924
12,850	12,900	1,931	1,931
12,900	12,950	1,939	1,939
12,950	13,000	1,946	1,946
13,000			
13,000	13,050	1,954	1,954
13,050	13,100	1,961	1,961
13,100	13,150	1,969	1,969
13,150	13,200	1,976	1,976
13,200	13,250	1,984	1,984
13,250	13,300	1,991	1,991
13,300	13,350	1,999	1,999
13,350	13,400	2,006	2,006
13,400	13,450	2,014	2,014
13,450	13,500	2,021	2,021
13,500	13,550	2,029	2,029
13,550	13,600	2,036	2,036
13,600	13,650	2,044	2,044
13,650	13,700	2,051	2,051
13,700	13,750	2,059	2,059
13,750	13,800	2,066	2,066
13,800	13,850	2,074	2,074
13,850	13,900	2,081	2,081
13,900	13,950	2,089	2,089
13,950	14,000	2,096	2,096
14,000			
14,000	14,050	2,104	2,104
14,050	14,100	2,111	2,111
14,100	14,150	2,119	2,119
14,150	14,200	2,126	2,126
14,200	14,250	2,134	2,134
14,250	14,300	2,141	2,141
14,300	14,350	2,149	2,149
14,350	14,400	2,156	2,156
14,400	14,450	2,164	2,164
14,450	14,500	2,171	2,171
14,500	14,550	2,179	2,179
14,550	14,600	2,186	2,186
14,600	14,650	2,194	2,194
14,650	14,700	2,201	2,201
14,700	14,750	2,209	2,209
14,750	14,800	2,216	2,216
14,800	14,850	2,224	2,224
14,850	14,900	2,231	2,231
14,900	14,950	2,239	2,239
14,950	15,000	2,246	2,246

If Form 1040EZ, line 6, is— At least	But less than	Single	Married filing jointly
15,000			
15,000	15,050	2,254	2,254
15,050	15,100	2,261	2,261
15,100	15,150	2,269	2,269
15,150	15,200	2,276	2,276
15,200	15,250	2,284	2,284
15,250	15,300	2,291	2,291
15,300	15,350	2,299	2,299
15,350	15,400	2,306	2,306
15,400	15,450	2,314	2,314
15,450	15,500	2,321	2,321
15,500	15,550	2,329	2,329
15,550	15,600	2,336	2,336
15,600	15,650	2,344	2,344
15,650	15,700	2,351	2,351
15,700	15,750	2,359	2,359
15,750	15,800	2,366	2,366
15,800	15,850	2,374	2,374
15,850	15,900	2,381	2,381
15,900	15,950	2,389	2,389
15,950	16,000	2,396	2,396
16,000			
16,000	16,050	2,404	2,404
16,050	16,100	2,411	2,411
16,100	16,150	2,419	2,419
16,150	16,200	2,426	2,426
16,200	16,250	2,434	2,434
16,250	16,300	2,441	2,441
16,300	16,350	2,449	2,449
16,350	16,400	2,456	2,456
16,400	16,450	2,464	2,464
16,450	16,500	2,471	2,471
16,500	16,550	2,479	2,479
16,550	16,600	2,486	2,486
16,600	16,650	2,494	2,494
16,650	16,700	2,501	2,501
16,700	16,750	2,509	2,509
16,750	16,800	2,516	2,516
16,800	16,850	2,524	2,524
16,850	16,900	2,531	2,531
16,900	16,950	2,539	2,539
16,950	17,000	2,546	2,546
17,000			
17,000	17,050	2,554	2,554
17,050	17,100	2,561	2,561
17,100	17,150	2,569	2,569
17,150	17,200	2,576	2,576
17,200	17,250	2,584	2,584
17,250	17,300	2,591	2,591
17,300	17,350	2,599	2,599
17,350	17,400	2,606	2,606
17,400	17,450	2,614	2,614
17,450	17,500	2,621	2,621
17,500	17,550	2,629	2,629
17,550	17,600	2,636	2,636
17,600	17,650	2,644	2,644
17,650	17,700	2,651	2,651
17,700	17,750	2,659	2,659
17,750	17,800	2,666	2,666
17,800	17,850	2,674	2,674
17,850	17,900	2,681	2,681
17,900	17,950	2,689	2,689
17,950	18,000	2,696	2,696

If Form 1040EZ, line 6, is— At least	But less than	Single	Married filing jointly
18,000			
18,000	18,050	2,704	2,704
18,050	18,100	2,711	2,711
18,100	18,150	2,719	2,719
18,150	18,200	2,726	2,726
18,200	18,250	2,734	2,734
18,250	18,300	2,741	2,741
18,300	18,350	2,749	2,749
18,350	18,400	2,756	2,756
18,400	18,450	2,764	2,764
18,450	18,500	2,771	2,771
18,500	18,550	2,779	2,779
18,550	18,600	2,786	2,786
18,600	18,650	2,794	2,794
18,650	18,700	2,801	2,801
18,700	18,750	2,809	2,809
18,750	18,800	2,816	2,816
18,800	18,850	2,824	2,824
18,850	18,900	2,831	2,831
18,900	18,950	2,839	2,839
18,950	19,000	2,846	2,846
19,000			
19,000	19,050	2,854	2,854
19,050	19,100	2,861	2,861
19,100	19,150	2,869	2,869
19,150	19,200	2,876	2,876
19,200	19,250	2,884	2,884
19,250	19,300	2,891	2,891
19,300	19,350	2,899	2,899
19,350	19,400	2,906	2,906
19,400	19,450	2,914	2,914
19,450	19,500	2,921	2,921
19,500	19,550	2,929	2,929
19,550	19,600	2,936	2,936
19,600	19,650	2,944	2,944
19,650	19,700	2,951	2,951
19,700	19,750	2,959	2,959
19,750	19,800	2,966	2,966
19,800	19,850	2,974	2,974
19,850	19,900	2,981	2,981
19,900	19,950	2,989	2,989
19,950	20,000	2,996	2,996
20,000			
20,000	20,050	3,004	3,004
20,050	20,100	3,011	3,011
20,100	20,150	3,019	3,019
20,150	20,200	3,026	3,026
20,200	20,250	3,034	3,034
20,250	20,300	3,041	3,041
20,300	20,350	3,049	3,049
20,350	20,400	3,056	3,056
20,400	20,450	3,064	3,064
20,450	20,500	3,071	3,071
20,500	20,550	3,079	3,079
20,550	20,600	3,086	3,086
20,600	20,650	3,094	3,094
20,650	20,700	3,101	3,101
20,700	20,750	3,109	3,109
20,750	20,800	3,116	3,116
20,800	20,850	3,124	3,124
20,850	20,900	3,131	3,131
20,900	20,950	3,139	3,139
20,950	21,000	3,146	3,146

CHAPTER 23   Taxes and Social Security

ACTIVITY 23-4	**Workplace Competencies**

ACTIVITY 23-4
Making Contributions to Social Security

Workplace Competencies

Systems:
Monitoring and Correcting Performance

Objective: To practice figuring out Social Security contributions and to verify accumulated amounts of Social Security taxes paid.

During your work life, you will pay a percentage of your earnings to the Social Security program. If you are employed, Social Security payments are withheld from your pay and sent to the federal government by your employer. If you are self-employed, you will pay both the employee's share and the employer's share of Social Security taxes. If you are a full-time self-employed person, you send payment for both parts of the tax to the federal government in quarterly tax payments (April 15, June 15, September 15, and January 15).

For this activity, read the case studies below. Then answer the questions that follow.

Case 1   Suppose you contract with 15 home owners to maintain their lawns for three months during the summer. Since you have a contract to work, you are considered self-employed. Your earnings for the summer are $2,700. To determine the amount of Social Security taxes you owe, use the self-employed tax rate of 15.3 percent.

1. How much money will you pay for Social Security taxes? _____

2. When and how will you make this payment?

_____

_____

Case 2   Suppose your brother worked for City Plumbing during the summer and earned $1,500. Use the employee tax rate of 7.65 percent to determine his Social Security tax.

1. How much money does your brother owe for Social Security tax? _____

2. How much money should his employer pay? _____

3. How will the payments be made? _____

_____

_____

CHAPTER *23* Taxes and Social Security

ACTIVITY 23-5	**Research**

Interviewing a Social Security Representative

Objective: To learn about the Social Security program and how it works.

Managers and representatives from local Social Security offices often talk with groups of people about the Social Security program. Discussion usually involves how the program works, who pays into the program, and the benefits it provides for young people, the disabled, and retired persons. With your teacher, invite a representative from the nearest office to meet with your class. Prepare your interview questions in advance. Some questions are included here. If you have other questions, write them on the next page.

As the representative speaks with your class, make notes and then answer the questions below.

1. How many years must someone work to have disability coverage?

_____

_____

_____

2. What persons are not covered by Social Security?

_____

_____

_____

3. How many years must someone contribute to the Social Security program to receive maximum benefits when they retire?

_____

_____

_____

4. How do you avoid errors in recording earnings of workers?

_____

_____

_____

_____

5. How can I check to be sure that my earnings and taxes paid are recorded correctly?

_____

_____

_____

_____

6. How does someone apply for Social Security benefits?

_____

_____

_____

_____

7. To whom must I give my Social Security number? How should the number be guarded to avoid misuse?

_____

_____

_____

_____

8. If I'm asked for my Social Security number when I make a purchase at a store and pay for it with a check, am I required to give the number?

_____

_____

_____

_____

(Continued on next page)

Other Questions

List additional questions here, or use this space to write other information you learned from the Social Security representative during the interview.

_____

_____

_____

_____

_____

_____

_____

_____

_____

_____

_____

_____

_____

_____

_____

_____

_____

_____

_____

_____

_____

_____

CHAPTER 24 Adapting to Change

ACTIVITY 24-1	**Foundation Skills**
How to Get a Raise	*Thinking Skills:* *Reasoning*

Objective: To learn how experienced workers get raises.

From reading the textbook chapter, you know that job success depends on doing your job well and demonstrating that you can handle responsibility. Some companies evaluate all their employees at least once a year and determine whether their work merits a raise. Other companies may not have as formal a system of performance reviews. In these companies, you may have to learn how to ask for a raise that you think you deserve.

Read the example that follows to learn how *not* to ask for a raise.

"If you have some time, I'd like to talk with you," Lori said to her boss, Mr. Larson.

"Certainly. I have a few minutes now. What's on your mind?" he asked.

"I need a raise," said Lori. "Right now I'm not able to meet expenses—what with rent, car payments, and a daughter to support. I feel that I've been working hard these last six months. When we were behind schedule, I put in a lot of overtime. You said yourself that I'm the best paste-up artist you've ever had work for you. I figured out that I will need at least $1.50 an hour more."

"If I gave you that," said Mr. Larson quietly, "you'd be making more than others with more experience. You realize we can't give pay raises on the basis of everyone's living expenses. I know you've been doing a good job though. Let me think some more about this, and I'll talk with you later."

Lori did receive a raise, but it wasn't for the amount she requested. She also realized she made some mistakes when she asked for the raise.

1. What were the mistakes Lori made?

_____

_____

2. What could Lori have done differently to have achieved a more positive outcome?

_____

_____

_____

_____

_____

_____

(Continued on next page)

Now that you have read an example of how *not* to ask for a raise, talk to an experienced worker for his/her suggestions on how to ask for an increase in pay. Read the questions below to the experienced worker and write the answers in the blanks provided.

Name of Worker _____

1. What conditions would cause you to feel that you deserved a pay raise?

_____

_____

2. When is a good time to ask for a pay raise?

_____

3. Should you ask for a specific amount? Why or why not?

_____

_____

4. Should you try to find out what other workers are paid before you ask for a raise? If so, how do you do this tactfully?

_____

_____

5. Will you usually take on more responsibility if you receive a raise?

_____

_____

6. Should you tell your employer why you think you deserve the raise? Why or why not?

_____

_____

7. If you are denied a raise, what should you do?

_____

_____

8. Do you have any other suggestions about asking for a pay raise?

_____

_____

CHAPTER 24 Adapting to Change

ACTIVITY 24-2	**Foundation Skills**
What Would You Do If . . . ?	*Thinking Skills: Reasoning*

Objective: To think about situations that could affect promotions and personal progress toward your career goals.

There is no way to predict what problems and questions will confront you as you pursue your career goals. The following case studies describe some common types of difficult situations people encounter on the job. Read each case study carefully, then answer the questions that follow it. Doing this activity may some-day help you handle a problem that stands between you and your career goals.

Case 1   Tom and Betty are tellers at the same bank. Tom had already worked at the bank a year when Betty was hired. He was asked to help train her. Tom knows the bank has been trying to promote more women, and he resents Betty's presence. If he trains her well, she may get the promotion he is hoping for. Betty doesn't understand why Tom is so cold toward her.

1. What would you do if you were Tom? Why?

_____

_____

_____

_____

2. What would you do if you were Betty? Why?

_____

_____

_____

_____

Case 2   Camille is a young reporter for her hometown newspaper. She is a good journalist. But she's unhappy because she hasn't had an opportunity to cover her real interest—sports. Most of her assignments have been for the family section of the paper. Today the news editor asked Camille to replace the courts and city council reporter, who is going on vacation. Camille is not really interested in either the courts or the city council.

(Continued on next page)

If you were Camille, what would you tell the news editor? Why?

_____

_____

_____

Case 3 Six months ago, when Bert was hired as a clerk in an athletic equipment store, he thought he had it made. The store was part of a large chain, and Bert's long-range goal was to manage one of these stores. Bert was good at his job, but a few months later business began to fall off. Last week Bert's boss told him that there just wasn't enough business to justify such a large staff. Since Bert was the last one hired, he would be the one to be laid off.

1. How would you feel if you were Bert? Why?

_____

_____

_____

_____

2. If you were Bert, would you give up your goal? Can you think of any ways that Bert might try to meet his goal in spite of his setback?

_____

_____

_____

Case 4 Gerald really wanted to be a commercial artist, but he knew that there would be a great deal of competition for jobs in commercial art. Afraid that he would be unable to find a job as an artist, Gerald looked for and found an office job as an administrative assistant. At his first performance evaluation, Gerald's boss pointed out that his word processing and other computer skills were not quite what they should be, and that no one could figure out his filing system. Gerald's boss wasn't sure Gerald had either the aptitude or the interest for his work. Gerald knew that his boss was right.

If you were Gerald, what would you do? Why?

_____

_____

_____

CHAPTER 24 Adapting to Change

ACTIVITY 24-3	**Foundation Skills**
Learning How to Reduce Stress	*Personal Qualities: Self-Management*

Objective: To learn how to reduce stress by setting realistic goals.

As you take on more responsibilities, you will need to cope with stress. You know from your text that one of the major causes of stress is the inability to reach personal goals. One technique you can use for reducing stress is to set realistic goals for yourself. You have already set some short-, medium-, and long-range career goals. In this activity, you are to set some specific and realistic goals for the other four parts of your lifestyle—family, friends, spiritual well-being, and leisure activities.

For your short-term goals, make up a list under each category of things you wish to accomplish this month. For your medium-term goals, list things you want to accomplish within six months. Your long-term goals will be what you want to achieve a year from now.

After you have made your list of goals, place a check mark beside the ones that have the highest priority for you. Then in the space next to these goals, write down specifically how you can achieve them.

Goal Setting

Short-Term Goals	How To Achieve
Family	
Friends	
Spiritual well-being	
Leisure activities	
Medium-Term Goals	
Family	
Friends	
Spiritual well-being	
Leisure activities	
Long-Term Goals	
Family	
Friends	
Spiritual well-being	
Leisure activities	

CHAPTER 24 Adapting to Change

ACTIVITY 24-4	Workplace Competencies
Planning for Lifelong Learning	*Systems: Improving and Designing Systems*

Objective: To design a plan for continued learning to help you meet career goals.

With changes in technology and in the way companies operate, you may need to learn different skills throughout your career. If you have an organized system for continued learning, you are more likely to be successful in lifelong learning.

Choose a career that you are considering and describe it in the space below. Review occupation descriptions to learn what skills are needed for an entry-level position in the field. Then find out the skills needed to advance to higher-level positions in that field. For example, in five years you may want to be in a supervisory position within your career field; in ten years, in a management position. What are the additional job skills that you'll need to gain these positions? Use the form below to chart the skills you'll need at each career level, and design a plan for how you will acquire these skills. For example, your plan might include regular college courses or special training seminars. Less formal training might include the magazines and newspapers you read to keep up-to-date in your field.

Career (briefly describe) _____

I. Entry-level skills needed (list job skills for your career):

_____

_____

_____

_____

Plan for acquiring skills needed (describe how you will learn skills, from on-the-job to formal training):

_____

_____

_____

Time required for training:

_____

_____

_____

II. Skills needed in five years (list job skills for advancing in your career):

_____

_____

_____

Plan for acquiring skills needed (describe how you will learn skills, from on-the-job to formal training):

_____

_____

_____

Time required for training:

_____

_____

_____

III. Skills needed in ten years (use skills for managers or senior positions within your career field):

_____

_____

_____

Plan for acquiring skills needed (describe how you will learn skills, from on-the-job to formal training):

_____

_____

_____

Time required for training:

_____

_____

_____

CHAPTER 24 Adapting to Change

ACTIVITY 24-5	**Research**

What to Do When You Need Career Help

Objective: To learn about the career assistance offered by different types of career professionals.

Whether you're seeking your first job or looking for a different career, at some time you may want to use the services of career professionals. These are the people and companies whose business is to offer career advice and counseling. Four different types of companies that offer career services are career counselors, career-marketing firms, outplacement firms, and résumé preparation services.

For this activity, you are to research the four types of career services and determine how their services differ. For references, use career books from your school and local libraries. Go through your telephone Yellow Pages and search the World Wide Web to find examples of each type of company. Telephone and ask for information about what they do. Use the space below to record your findings.

Career Counselors

1. What are the names and telephone numbers of one or two local career counselors?

_____

_____

2. What services do career counselors offer?

_____

_____

_____

_____

3. What professional credentials should you look for in a career counselor; in other words, what special training does the person have to advise you on your career?

_____

_____

_____

_____

4. What do career counselors charge for their services?

_____

_____

Career-Marketing (Job Search) Firms

1. What are the names and telephone numbers of one or two local career marketing firms?

_____

_____

2. What services do career marketing firms offer?

_____

_____

_____

_____

3. What professional credentials should you look for in the people who work for career marketing firms?

_____

_____

_____

4. What do career marketing firms charge for their services?

_____

_____

Outplacement Firms

1. What are the names and telephone numbers of one or two local outplacement firms?

_____

_____

2. What services do outplacement firms offer?

_____

_____

_____

_____

(Continued on next page)

3. What professional credentials should you look for in the people who work for outplacement firms?

_____

_____

_____

4. What do outplacement firms charge for their services?

_____

_____

_____

Résumé Preparation Services

1. What are the names, telephone numbers, and/or URLs of one or two résumé preparation services?

_____

_____

_____

2. What services do résumé preparation services offer?

_____

_____

_____

_____

3. What professional credentials should you look for in people who work for résumé preparation services?

_____

_____

_____

_____

4. What do résumé preparation services charge?

_____

_____

CHAPTER 25 Balancing Work and Personal LIfe

ACTIVITY 25-1	**Foundation Skills**
Estimating Expenses for Living on Your Own	*Basic Skills: Mathematics*

Objective: To estimate the amount of money you will need to live on your own.

Young people are often eager to be out on their own. Before you move into your own place, you need to consider what it will cost and whether you can afford it. This activity will give you some idea of how much you can expect to pay for a furnished or unfurnished apartment in your area.

First, using the "Apartments for Rent" section of your newspaper or local apartment rental booklets, determine an average rent per month for both furnished and unfurnished apartments. Consider only 1- or 2-bedroom units. Call to find out about security deposits, and calculate an average amount. Write that information in the form.

Next, list all the items of furniture you would need for an unfurnished apartment. Write your estimate of the cost of each item and where you could buy it for that price. Decide whether, on average, it is cheaper to rent a furnished apartment or an unfurnished one. After completing the form below, answer the questions that follow.

Average Rent		
For Furnished Apartment _____	For Unfurnished Apartment _____	
Average Security Deposit _____		
Furniture Needed for an Unfurnished Apartment		
Name of Item	**Estimated Cost**	**Where Available**

1. What are your estimated costs for moving into a furnished apartment?

_____

_____

2. How much money would you need to buy your own furniture and move into an unfurnished apartment?

_____

CHAPTER 25 Balancing Work and Personal LIfe

ACTIVITY 25-2	Foundation Skills
Monthly Budget for Living on Your Own	*Basic Skills: Mathematics*

Objective: To learn how much you can expect to pay in monthly living expenses for living on your own.

Use the rental amount you calculated for Activity 25-1 or select a furnished or unfurnished apartment from your local newspaper or apartment rentals booklet. Then complete the monthly budget below.

Item	Estimated Cost per Month	Item	Estimated Cost per Month
Household Expenses:		**Personal:**	
Rent	_____	Laundry & dry cleaning	_____
Furniture (payments)	_____	Magazines & newspapers	_____
Telephone	_____	Recreation	_____
Electricity	_____	Church & charities	_____
Heating	_____	Gifts (birthdays, etc.)	_____
Water	_____	Emergencies	_____
Trash collection	_____	Other _____	_____
Other utilities (cable TV, etc.)	_____	Total	_____
Household supplies (soaps, cleaners, etc.)	_____	**Total of first column**	_____
Other _____	_____		
		Grand total	_____
Food & Transportation			
Food	_____		
Car payments	_____		
Car repairs	_____		
Gas & oil	_____		
Bus fare	_____		
Other _____	_____		
Total	_____		

1. How much will you need to earn each month to pay your monthly expenses if the recommended 25 percent of gross monthly income is used to pay rent?

_____

2. Subtract remaining expenses from the monthly income you calculated. Will you have money for savings or for expenses if they are 10 percent higher than your estimates?

_____

CHAPTER *25* Balancing Work and Personal Life

ACTIVITY 25-3	**Foundation Skills**
Examining a Lease	*Basic Skills: Reading*

Objective: To learn what to look for when reading a lease.

A lease is a contract between a landlord and a renter that states the responsibilities of each party. When you rent an apartment, you will be expected to sign a lease. Ask to read any lease before signing it. If you have questions about some of the terms or conditions in a lease, ask to have them explained.

Read the sample lease below. Then answer the questions that follow.

Apartment Lease

Date	Term of Lease		Monthly Rent	Security Deposit
	Beginning	Ending		
Jan. 15, 2002	*Feb 1, 2002*	*Feb 1, 2003*	*$400.00*	*$400.00*

Agreements and Covenants

1. RENT: Tenant shall pay to the Lessor the monthly rent set forth above, on, or before the first day of each month. *Time is of the essence.* The Lessor will assess a late charge of $5 per day for rent five days overdue. The amount of rent will remain as stated above for the term of the lease, the only exception being a case in which Lessor's real estate taxes are raised, at which time the Lessor may raise the rent one percent of increased assessment if he sees fit to do so.

2. NOTICES: Tenants agree to inform landlord one month in advance if they intend to move from said premises. Failure to provide proper notice will result in assessment of a $400 penalty by Lessor.

3. ALTERATIONS, ADDITIONS, FIXTURES, ETC.: Tenants will not make alterations or additions to walls or any part of the building, without written consent of the Lessor; and then, if granted, no fixtures may be removed from the walls. Tenants shall return to its original condition at his or her own expense any changes not approved in writing.

4. ACCESS: Lessor reserves the right to enter the Apartment for inspection and repair of property as needed, so long as the Tenants are in attendance. The Lessor may not enter during the Tenants' absence unless an emergency situation, defined as a situation in which the well being of the Apartment is in immediate jeopardy, arises.

5. ASSIGNMENT, SUBLETTING, AND RELETTING: This lease is not assignable, nor is subletting permitted.

(Continued on next page)

1. What is the term of the lease (the length of time it covers)?

   _____

2. Who is the lessor?

   _____

3. Can the landlord raise the rent during the term of the lease? If so, under what conditions?

   _____

   _____

4. What happens if you are three days late paying your rent? Six days late?

   _____

   _____

5. How much notice must you give to the landlord before moving?

   _____

   _____

6. What happens if you fail to give proper notice of your intention to move?

   _____

   _____

7. Are you allowed to hang pictures on the walls?

   _____

   _____

8. Are you allowed to take anything you attach to a wall with you when you move?

   _____

   _____

9. Is the landlord allowed to enter the apartment during your absence?

   _____

10. Are you allowed to sublet the apartment?

    _____

CHAPTER 25 Balancing Work and Personal Life

ACTIVITY 25-4	**Workplace Competencies**
Looking for a Place to Rent	*Information:* *Acquiring and Evaluating Information*

Objective: To collect and organize information for use in evaluating places to rent.

One of the steps in the decision-making process you learned in your textbook is to gather information. For this activity, use the checklist on this page and the next page to collect information about apartments. You are to collect information on two apartments (make a copy of the checklist) and compare the features. You may want to pair up with a classmate to do this activity. Visit an apartment rental office and explain to the landlord or office staff that you are there for a class assignment. Ask if you may see an apartment. Then rate the apartment according to the factors on the checklist. Decide, with your partner, which apartment you like best. Discuss your findings with the rest of the class.

Apartment Checklist

Location _____

Outside Areas

Location and neighborhood
- ☐ Yes ☐ No **1.** Do you like the area?
- ☐ Yes ☐ No **2.** Is there enough privacy?
- ☐ Yes ☐ No **3.** Are the surrounding buildings in good condition?
- ☐ Yes ☐ No **4.** Would you feel comfortable living here?

Grounds around building
- ☐ Yes ☐ No **1.** Is there a yard?
- ☐ Yes ☐ No **2.** Will you need to mow the grass?
- ☐ Yes ☐ No **3.** Are the grounds free of litter and trash?

Exterior quality of building
- ☐ Yes ☐ No **1.** Is the building in good condition?
- ☐ Yes ☐ No **2.** Will you have to get the owner to make repairs?

Noise and air pollution
- ☐ Yes ☐ No **1.** Is there a great deal of traffic noise?
- ☐ Yes ☐ No **2.** Is the air clean?
- ☐ Yes ☐ No **3.** Do there seem to be many children or animals in the area?

Parking facilities
- ☐ Yes ☐ No **1.** Are there parking facilities?
- ☐ Yes ☐ No **2.** Will this cost extra?

Locked mailbox
- ☐ Yes ☐ No **1.** Is a locked mailbox available?

(Continued on next page)

Safety precautions

☐ Yes ☐ No **1.** Is the outside area safe to walk through, even at night?

Transportation

☐ Yes ☐ No **1.** Are bus stops or train, trolley, or subway stations within walking distance?

Recreation

☐ Yes ☐ No **1.** Are recreational facilities available nearby?

☐ Yes ☐ No **2.** Does the apartment complex have a pool, tennis court, or recreation room?

Inside Areas

Condition of hall and steps

☐ Yes ☐ No **1.** Are the hall and steps in good condition?

☐ Yes ☐ No **2.** Does it look like someone cleans regularly?

Fire escape

☐ Yes ☐ No **1.** Are there at least two ways to get out of the building?

Cleanliness

☐ Yes ☐ No **1.** Will you have to do a great deal of cleaning before you move in?

☐ Yes ☐ No **2.** Does it look like the place has been well cared for?

Room arrangement

☐ Yes ☐ No **1.** Do you like the floor plan?

☐ Yes ☐ No **2.** If you have a roommate, will your sleeping arrangements give each of you privacy?

Storage

☐ Yes ☐ No **1.** Is there enough room to store everything?

☐ Yes ☐ No **2.** Is there enough cabinet space in the kitchen?

☐ Yes ☐ No **3.** Are there many closets?

Condition of kitchen fixtures

☐ Yes ☐ No **1.** Do all furnished appliances work?

☐ Yes ☐ No **2.** Do cabinet doors and drawers work smoothly?

Condition of bathroom fixtures

☐ Yes ☐ No **1.** Is there a shower and a bath?

☐ Yes ☐ No **2.** Does the plumbing work properly?

☐ Yes ☐ No **3.** Was there plenty of pressure and hot water when you tried the faucets?

Condition of windows, screens, and locks

☐ Yes ☐ No **1.** Is there any broken glass?

☐ Yes ☐ No **2.** Do the windows close easily?

☐ Yes ☐ No **3.** Do the windows lock?

☐ Yes ☐ No **4.** Would the windows fit tightly for the winter?

☐ Yes ☐ No **5.** Are there screens for the summer?

CHAPTER 25 Balancing Work and Personal LIfe

ACTIVITY 25-5
Being a Good Citizen

Objective: To research ways you can become an informed and involved citizen.

To be a good citizen, you must be informed about issues affecting all people and involved in making decisions about those issues. One way to learn about issues in your community is to volunteer to help one or more nonprofit organizations that provide community services. For this activity, choose one of the following issues:

- Providing food and shelter for the homeless
- Providing shelter and counseling for battered women and children
- Creating awareness of the dangers of drinking and driving

Conduct research on the issue of your choice using a variety of resources. For example, you might check with your local library to find information on nonprofit organizations. If you have access to the Internet, you can conduct searches on the topic. Or you might talk with people in your community and ask them about local organizations. You might also contact local representatives of national agencies, such as United Way, and ask about the services the agency provides.

Conduct research to find answers to the questions below. Write your answers in the spaces provided. When you have finished your research, discuss your ideas with the class.

1. List five resources you used to find information about organizations in your community working on the topic you chose.

_____

_____

_____

_____

_____

2. Write down your ideas for how you can help with the topic you chose.

_____

_____

_____

(Continued on next page)

3. What will you have to do to carry out your ideas?

_____

_____

_____

_____

_____

4. How will you get others involved in your volunteer work?

_____

_____

_____

_____

_____

5. What can you do beyond your local community to help (for example, at the state or national level)?

_____

_____

_____

_____

_____

6. On a separate sheet of paper, write a letter to a government official stressing your concern with the topic you chose and asking what the government is doing to address the issue.